INTERNATIONAL SERIES OF MONOGRAPHS IN
EXPERIMENTAL PSYCHOLOGY
GENERAL EDITOR: H. J. EYSENCK

Volume 3

ATTENTION, AROUSAL AND THE ORIENTATION REACTION

Attention, Arousal and the Orientation Reaction

BY

R. LYNN

Department of Psychology
University of Exeter

PERGAMON PRESS

OXFORD · LONDON · EDINBURGH · NEW YORK
PARIS · FRANKFURT

Pergamon Press Ltd., Headington Hill Hall, Oxford
4 & 5 Fitzroy Square, London W.1

Pergamon Press (Scotland) Ltd., 2 & 3 Teviot Place, Edinburgh 1

Pergamon Press Inc., 44–01 21st Street, Long Island City, New York 11101

Pergamon Press S.A.R.L., 24 rue des Écoles, Paris 5^e

Pergamon Press GmbH, Kaiserstrasse 75, Frankfurt-am-Main

First edition 1966

Library of Congress Catalog Card No. 65-28389

PRINTED IN GREAT BRITAIN BY
Dawson & Goodall Ltd., Bath, England
2511/66

CONTENTS

CONTENTS

FOREWORD

IN RECENT years psychologists have become very interested in what Pavlov used to call the orienting reflex. Much of this work has been carried out in the U.S.S.R., and while some of the books and papers in which this work appeared have been translated, Western readers have not until now had an opportunity of seeing it all brought together in one volume. Dr. Lynn has undertaken this difficult and arduous duty and we are all indebted to him for doing it so well and so concisely.

As befits the followers of Pavlov, Russian psychologists have couched their interpretations and theories very much in physiological terms, and have elaborated neurological models of considerable interest. Some Western psychologists of course prefer the doctrine of the empty organism, but most would probably decline to throw away all the important contributions that recent work in this biological discipline has been able to make to psychological understanding. Dr. Lynn discusses and evaluates these theories and models and leaves little doubt that they form an important contribution to the development of this field.

It is particularly interesting to note that the logic of scientific development has led Russian workers to the field of individual differences. Here again of course Pavlov made a beginning but it was left to his successors, particularly Teplov, to carry out most of the experimental work needed and to clarify the theoretical position. In the Western world interest in individual differences has not on the whole penetrated to workers in the fields of physiological psychology and of neurology; this is a pity. There is little doubt that individual differences in excitation and inhibition underlie much of what we call "personality", and a full understanding of these individual differences would be of central importance to the development of scientific psychology. Dr. Lynn's discussion does full justice to the importance of this topic. Here, as throughout the book, he demonstrates that Russian writings can be made intelligible and even exciting when their themes are fully understood and properly digested. Dr. Lynn's book will be a God-send to all those interested in this field but put off by the odd nomenclature and the curious English usually found in translations from the Russian.

H. J. EYSENCK

ACKNOWLEDGEMENTS

I AM greatly indebted to Professor H. J. Eysenck and to Dr. I. Oswald for their critical reading of the first draft of this book.

CHAPTER 1

THE ORIENTATION REACTION

WHEN an animal is presented with a new stimulus it pricks up its ears, looks in the direction of the stimulus and alerts itself to deal with possible eventualities which the stimulus may herald. It is this response which Russian physiologists and psychologists call the "orientation reaction" and which is the subject of this book.

In the early years of the century the orientation reaction was a source of some embarrassment to Pavlov's students. They found that when they had perfected some conditioning technique and called in the professor to see it, the dog turned its attention—made an orientation reaction—to Pavlov instead of performing in the required manner. Beginning as an inconvenience, the orientation reaction eventually became a phenomenon of interest in its own right, and was extensively commented upon by Pavlov. At different times he called it the "investigating" and "what-is-it?" reaction, and in one passage describes it as follows:

> It is this reflex which brings about the immediate response in man and animals to the slightest changes in the world around them, so that they immediately orientate their appropriate receptor organ in accordance with the perceptible quality in the agent bringing about the change, making a full investigation of it. The biological significance of this reflex is obvious. If the animal were not provided with such a reflex its life would hang at any moment by a thread. In man this reflex has been greatly developed with far reaching results, being represented in its highest form by inquisitiveness—the parent of that scientific method through which we hope one day to come to a true orientation in knowledge of the world around us. (PAVLOV, 1927)

While some may feel that Pavlov was being somewhat over-enthusiastic in regarding man's scientific and creative achievements as a developed form of the simple orientation reactions of animals, nevertheless a mechanism for paying attention to novel stimuli must be of great significance for survival.

1

COMPONENTS OF THE ORIENTATION REACTION

Apart from the simple turning towards the source of the novel stimulus, it has become evident that the orientation reaction involves a large number of physiological changes. The purpose of these changes, in general terms, is to make the animal more sensitive to incoming stimuli so that it is better equipped to discern what is happening, and to mobilize the body for whatever action may be necessary; for "fight or flight" as Cannon expressed it. More formally, the components of the orientation reaction can be categorized as follows:

I. Increase in sensitivity of sense organs

(i) The pupil dilates.

(ii) There are photochemical changes in the retina lowering the threshold for intensity of light.

(iii) The auditory threshold is lowered; in man the lowering is of the order of 4–10 db (Gershuni *et al.*, 1960).

Direct evidence for the increase in sensitivity of the sense organs during the orientation reaction is shown by the following experiment. The subject's visual threshold for motor response and alpha-rhythm blocking is first obtained by the usual psychophysical methods. A test stimulus 0·8 below threshold is then presented and no response is given. Then a sound is presented and the subject gives an orientation reaction. The visual test stimulus is now given again and this time the subject gives a reaction (Sokolov, 1960). There is a very large body of Russian literature on this topic of the effects of one stimulus on the threshold for another, which has been extensively reviewed by London (1954). Some of the results are very remarkable; generally the effect of the first stimulus is to lower the threshold for the second; the results have been confirmed by Western investigators (Yerkes, 1904; Symons, 1963). Many of these results become explicable in terms of the physiological mechanisms of the orientation reaction advanced by Sokolov and summarized in the next chapter. Comparative investigations show that amphibians show the intersensory facilitation phenomenon—for example, the responses of toads to equilibratory stimuli increase with light (Birukov, 1951). Yerkes (1904) maintained that intersensory facilitation could not be obtained in animals lower than the frog and inferred that the mechanisms involved emerged at the amphibian level.

While it is an increase in sensory sensitivity during the orientation reaction that is stressed by Sokolov, it should be observed that the presentation of novel stimuli may also in certain circumstances entail a decrease in sensitivity. One example of this is presented by Hernández-Peón, Scherrer and Jouvet (1956) in an experiment in which recordings were taken from the cochlear nucleus of a cat during auditory stimulation by clicks. When the cat is relaxed a large response is obtained from the cochlear nucleus. If the cat is now shown mice in a jar an orientation reaction occurs, and at the same time the evoked potentials from the cochlear nucleus in response to the clicks greatly diminish. This result indicates the existence of some mechanism whereby during attention to one stimulus, information about irrelevant stimuli is blocked or reduced at a very peripheral level. This inhibitory mechanism appears to be directed from a centre in the mesencephalic reticular formation, since destruction of this area by lesions or impairment by drugs abolishes the effect (Hernández-Peón, 1960). How this centre determines whether the clicks are relevant or irrelevant to the object of attention raises a rather considerable problem.

II. Changes in the skeletal muscles that direct sense organs

The animal turns its head towards the source of stimulus, pricks up its ears and sniffs.

III. Changes in general skeletal musculature

Ongoing reactions are temporarily arrested and general muscle tonus rises, increasing readiness for activity in the skeletal muscles. There is an increase in electromyographic muscular electrical activity.

IV. EEG changes

The EEG changes towards increased arousal, i.e. faster and lower amplitude activity.

V. Vegetative changes

    (i) Vasoconstriction occurs in the limbs, vasodilation in the head.
    (ii) The galvanic skin reaction occurs.

(iii) Respiration rates: there is a delay, followed by increase in amplitude and decrease in frequency (Davis *et al.*, 1955).

(iv) Heart rate: these reactions are very variable. In human subjects the heart rate slows; this is a somewhat paradoxical reaction, since in most other situations where human subjects are activated to perform tasks, the heart rate increases. Nevertheless, the decrease in heart rate when the subject is required to pay attention is well substantiated by Western workers (Lacey, 1959, p. 147; Notterman, 1953; Davis, 1957). Davis reports the heart slowing as part of the "*P*" pattern of reaction, obtained in its purest form when the male college student examines a picture of a nude female.

The heart slowing reaction is also obtained in dogs, sheep (Liddell, 1959, p. 146) and cats (Maclean, 1959, p. 147), but the goat reacts with heart rate acceleration (Liddell, 1959, p. 146).

Petelina (1958) distinguishes (a) the "compression reaction", given by dogs to the first presentation of a tone in which breathing is interrupted and then becomes shallower and slow and heart rate decreases; and (b) the "stimulation reaction", occurring on later presentations of the tone, with opposite effects. Flashes of light evoke the "stimulation reaction" straightaway. This distinction probably corresponds to the startle reaction – orientation reaction. (see below).

GENERALIZED AND LOCALIZED ORIENTATION REACTIONS

Sokolov distinguishes two varieties of orientation reaction.

(1) *Generalized orientation reaction*. This is the reaction elicited first and is characterized by (a) higher frequency EEG rhythms over the whole of the cerebral cortex; (b) the increase in arousal may last for some fairly considerable time, say an hour or so in the case of a drowsy person suddenly aroused by an intense stimulus; and (c) it habituates quickly, typically after 10–15 trials. This is the reaction also observed by Sharpless and Jasper (1956) in cats and called by them the *tonic* arousal reaction.

(2) *Localized orientation reaction*. With further repetitions of the stimulus the generalized orientation reaction becomes habituated and there remains the localized orientation reaction (phasic arousal reaction of Sharpless and Jasper). It differs from the generalized orientation in that (i) the EEG desynchronization is confined to the cortical area of the particular sensory modality and there are no

EEG effects in the rest of the cortex; (ii) the reaction subsides quickly, lasting for about one minute; (iii) it is more resistant to habituation, surviving for some 30 or so trials.

Whether the generalized or localized orientation reaction occurs depends also on the state of the subject. When the subject is in a drowsy state or asleep, the new stimulus elicits the generalized reaction. But if the subject is already alert or excited, the orientation reaction occurs only in its localized form. Precisely the same distinction between a generalized and localized orientation reaction has been drawn by Gastaut (1957).

INDIVIDUAL DIFFERENCES IN THE ORIENTATION REACTION

All these components of the orientation reaction do not necessarily occur in all subjects; there are individual differences in which combinations occur and in the strength of the reactions. A typical experimental finding is presented by Voronin and Sokolov (1960) in which 100 human subjects were stimulated with a tone (1000 cps, 50 db). Alpha-rhythm blocking in the occipital area was obtained in 85 subjects, Rolandic rhythm blocking in 53, PGRs in 95, eye movements in 42, changes in respiration rates in 63, and an increase in digital flexors' tonus in 1 subject only. All the components of the orientation reaction (except for the muscle reaction) were present in 11 subjects.

FUNCTIONS OF THE ORIENTATION REACTION

The function of the orientation reaction is to prepare the animal to deal with the novel stimulus. For many of the components of the reaction this preparatory function is straightforward. Activities under way are stopped so that they will not interfere with any action that needs to be taken and the muscles are mobilized for activity. The sense organs become more sensitive and the head is turned towards the source of stimulation in order to maximize incoming information. The autonomic components of the reaction likewise prepare the body for emergency action. The PGR is somewhat puzzling in its lack of any apparent purpose. Darrow (1936) has suggested it may facilitate grip and Sokolov (1963a) that it increases cutaneous sensitivity. The pause in respiration, according to Sokolov (1963a), increases olfactory sensitivity.

The purpose of the EEG desynchronization has recently become evident from the work of Lindsley (1960), who has shown that reaction times are fastest when the stimulus coincides with a particular phase of the alpha-rhythm cycle. It is suggested by Berlyne (1960) that the function of desynchronization is to ensure that the stimulus at any moment reaches a group of nerves whose cycle is at its optimum, thus speeding up reaction time.

There is evidence from Western laboratories to support Sokolov's view that the orientation reaction does mobilize the animal for more efficient action. Some of the most striking experiments have been carried out by Lindsley and his associates at Los Angeles. In one of these, monkeys were trained to discriminate two objects exposed tachistoscopically and to react to the correct one. Increasing arousal by stimulation of the reticular formation through implanted electrodes had the effect of decreasing reaction time (Fuster, 1957). In another experiment visual reaction times were reduced in human subjects from an average of 280 msec to 206 msec when an auditory signal preceded the visual stimulus by at least three-tenths of a second. It is assumed that the auditory warning signal has an arousing – orientation function which is responsible for its facilitatory effect.

OTHER REACTIONS

The orientation reaction is not the only response that can be made to novel stimuli. Two other responses are possible, namely adaptive and defensive reactions. Typically the orientation reaction occurs first and is replaced after a number of trials by an adaptive reaction in the case of weak and moderate stimuli and a defensive reaction in the case of intense stimuli. One of the striking differences between orientation reactions and adaptive and defensive reactions is that only the orientation reaction is subject to quick habituation.

(1) *Adaptive Reactions*

Adaptive reactions differ from orientation reactions in a number of ways. Whereas the effect of the orientation reaction is to increase sensitivity to stimulation (a positive feedback reaction), the effect of adaptive reactions is to preserve equilibrium (negative feedback). The effect has of course long been known as a homeostatic mechanism. In the case of intense stimuli the adaptive reaction dampens down stimulation, whereas when stimulation falls in intensity it works to increase the effect of stimulation. Some examples of the adaptive reaction are shown below:

Stimulus	Adaptive reaction	Effect of reaction
Heat	Vasodilation	Facilitation of heat loss
Cold	Vasoconstriction	Facilitation of heat retention
Decrease in illumination	(1) Pupil dilation (2) Dark adaptation	Increases light influx Increases retinal sensitivity
Increase in illumination	(1) Pupil contraction (2) Light adaptation	Decreases light influx Decreases retinal sensitivity

These are adaptive reactions in the sense organs. But it should be noted that rather similar homeostatic reactions occur in the specific sensory tracts to the cortex. This effect, first extensively reported by Hernández-Peón (1960) and termed by him "afferent neuronal habituation", takes the form of a decrease in the amplitude of evoked potentials recorded from electrodes implanted in the specific sensory pathways and relay nuclei. Its existence has been demonstrated by Hernández-Peón and his associates in the auditory, visual and cutaneous tracts. Like the adaptive reactions in the sense organs, afferent neuronal habituation also only occurs after the initial orientation reaction has been extinguished (Gershuni et al., 1960).

The adaptive reaction can therefore be distinguished from the orientation reaction in that (a) it is local rather than generalized and confined to the sense organ stimulated, and the specific sensory tracts from the sense organ to the cortex; (b) it has a homeostatic negative feedback rather than a positive feedback effect; and (c) it does not habituate with repeated stimulation.

(2) Defensive Reactions

The effects of an intense stimulus which in everyday parlance startles the animal has given rise to a perplexing proliferation of terms, viz. startle reaction (Landis and Hunt, 1939), defensive reaction (Sokolov, 1960), orientation reflex (Konorski, 1960), as well as other reactions which may or may not be orientation reactions, such as arousal reactions, alerting reactions and surprise reactions. It seems likely that many of these terms are synonymous and that there are in fact two principal kinds of reactions, namely orientation reactions and defensive reactions.

The defensive reaction appears to correspond in part to what is called in Western literature the startle reaction, which has been described most fully by Strauss (1929) and confirmed by Landis and Hunt (1939). Landis and Hunt induced startle reactions by firing a revolver behind the subject and described the reaction in detail following photographic recording of it. It consists of blinking of the eyes, head movement forward, widening of the mouth, raising and drawing forward of the shoulders, abduction of the upper arms, bending of the elbows, pronation of the lower arms, flexion of the fingers, forward movement of the trunk, contraction of the abdomen and bending of the knees. The reaction has a latency of about 0·5 of a second and lasts for about the same time. The eyeblink always occurs, but not all the other components of the reaction are invariably present. This reaction seems to be a special case of Sokolov's defensive reaction and hence we have combined the two terms.

Several distinctions may be drawn between the orientation reaction and the startle – defensive reaction. To particularize:

(1) *Overt bodily reactions.* In the orientation reaction the body is turned towards the source of stimulation. In the startle – defensive reaction the overt reactions (according to Sokolov, 1960) may include running away from the stimulus, aggressive reactions, or freezing.

(2) *Physiological reactions.* Many of these are the same in the orientation and startle – defensive reactions, since the purpose of both is to mobilize the animal for efficient action. The chief distinction emphasized by Sokolov is that whereas in the orientation reaction there is vasoconstriction in the blood vessels in the limbs and vasodilation in the head, in the startle – defensive reaction there is vasoconstriction in the head as well as in the limbs. The startle reaction of Landis and Hunt (1939) includes the PGR and increase in blood pressure. The physiological characteristics of the startle – defensive and orientation reactions have also been discussed by Gastaut and Roger (1960). He concludes that in the startle – defensive reaction there is eyeblinking with contraction of the orbicular muscles of the eyelids and brief contraction of the skeletal muscles (for something less than a second), especially in the upper limbs,

neck and face. Autonomic components of this reaction unclude a pause in respiration, increased heart rate and PGR. The EEG reaction is a short and generalized desynchronization. According to Gastaut the orientation reaction differs from the startle – defensive reaction only in degree by being less intense. However, Gastaut identifies the startle – defensive reaction with Sokolov's generalized orientation reaction, whereas Sokolov distinguishes the reactions on the basis of the vasoreactions in the head (vasoconstriction in the startle – defensive reaction, vasodilation in the generalized orientation reaction).

(3) *Introspective attention reactions.* The distinction made many years ago by introspectionist psychologists between primary and secondary attention is in many ways similar to the startle – defensive and orientation reactions. A typical example concerns a geologist walking with a non-geological friend in a gorge. A boulder suddenly falls down in front of them and elicits in both "primary attention", the startle – defensive reaction. Continuing their walk they come across an unusual rock formation. The non-geologist does not notice it, but the geologist immediately sees and investigates it. This is "secondary attention", the orientation reaction, including orientation towards the stimulus for the purpose of further investigation. Here it is a learned response and is elicited by stimuli which are familiar but whose meaning is still to some extent uncertain.

(4) *Affective reactions.* The magnitude of the physiological reactions in the startle – defensive reaction makes them unpleasant, with sensations of shock, suffocation, palpitations and fear. In the orientation reaction the more moderate reaction is accompanied by an agreeable rise in excitement and interest.

(5) *Habituation rates.* The orientation reaction habituates fairly quickly, after something of the order of 10–30 stimulations. The startle – defensive reaction habituates much more slowly (Sokolov, 1963a). Thus Moyer (1963) stimulated rats with six pistol shots a day at 30 sec intervals for five days. Apart from a lesser response on the second day, probably due to habituation to the experimental situation, there was no further habituation from the second to the fifth day.

Several variables control whether the animal makes an orientation reaction or a defensive reaction:

(1) The intensity of the stimulus. Very high intensity stimuli induce immediate defensive reactions.

B

(2) The number of repetitions of the stimulus. Moderately intense stimuli may produce orientation reactions for the first few trials and then defensive reactions.

(3) Signal value. If a stimulus acquires signal value, i.e. becomes a conditioned stimulus, it becomes more likely to evoke an orientation reaction at both lower intensities (where previously it evoked no reaction) and at higher intensities (Sokolov, 1963a). These phenomena are discussed more fully in Chapter 5.

Although the Russian division of arousal reactions into adaptive, orientation and defensive has a pleasing simplicity, Western research in this area indicates that the facts are somewhat more complex. One of the leading Western experimentalists, Davis (1957), confirms the Russian position as far as the arousal pattern to simple visual and auditory stimuli are concerned: these elicit the PGR, increase in muscle tension, vasoconstriction in the finger and vasodilation in the head. However, the presentation of pictures to human subjects elicits a variety of perplexing reactions. Pictures of nude females presented to male college students elicit vasoconstriction in both fingers and head, together with deceleration of heart rate; in the Russian system this would be classified as a defensive reaction, which would hardly seem appropriate to the stimulus. A picture of a starving man, on the other hand, elicits a qualitatively different reaction, including acceleration in heart rate. Female students react differently again. These are only examples of the many different patterns of autonomic reaction which can be obtained with different types of stimuli. Nevertheless the trichotomy of the Russian workers of adaptive, orientation and startle – defensive reactions may be useful as an initial classification.

STIMULI ELICITING THE ORIENTATION REACTION

The characteristics of stimuli eliciting the orientation reaction have been well collated by Berlyne (1960), who categorizes them as follows.

(1) *Novelty*. This is the overriding stimulus characteristic eliciting the orientation reaction. The obverse of this is of course the phenomenon of habituation, i.e. the fact that animals no longer pay any attention to familiar stimuli.

(2) *Intensity*. Stimuli of moderate to high intensity elicit orientation reactions and within this range the reaction obeys the

Pavlovian law of strength, that is, stronger stimuli elicit stronger reactions. But if stimuli become very intense they may elicit the startle – defensive reaction. But also increasing the intensity of the stimulus brings about a stage at which the reaction ceases to increase in size, called by Russian investigators the threshold of the breaking of the law of strength or the phase of equalization. With further increases in stimulus intensity the reaction decreases in size, following Pavlov's paradoxical phase. These effects have been reported in pigeons and rabbits by Zagorylko and Sollertinskaya (1958) using respiration rates, heart rates, EMGs and EEG reactions as indices of the orientation reaction.

(3) *Colour.* In human infants colour stimuli are more likely to elicit orientation reactions than grey (Valentine, 1914; Staples, 1932). The same is true of adults, according to Brandt (1944), who found subjects spend more time looking at red and white designs than at black and white ones.

(4) *Conditioned stimuli* (*signal stimuli*). A number of stimuli can elicit orientation reactions through learning. Probably the most striking example of this is the sound of one's name, but a number of words and phrases such as "Look out" and "Listen to this" act in the same way.

These conditioning effects have been demonstrated in animals by Russian workers. In these experiments a neutral stimulus comes to evoke an orientation reaction through association with another stimulus. For example, Narbutovich and Podkopaev (1936) presented a tone and a flash of light to dogs and found that the stimulus presented first came to evoke orientation reactions towards the source of the second. Orientation reactions to conditioned stimuli are fairly complex and are discussed in detail in Chapter 5.

(5) *Surprise.* Orientation reactions are frequently evoked by a surprising change in experimental conditions. Thus monkeys trained to find a particular reward such as a banana under a cup give pronounced orientation reactions when they find a lettuce there (Tinklepaugh, 1928).

A somewhat similar situation arises when stimuli habitually presented in a certain order suddenly occur in a different order (Soloveichik, 1928). An especially important example occurs in discrimination learning, when an animal finds that a generalized stimulus is not followed by reward (Grastyan, 1959).

It is not always easy to distinguish surprise as a variable from novelty, since frequently the two occur together. An experiment isolating surprise is reported by Berlyne (1961). Here the subject was presented with a diamond with lights at the four corners and instructed to watch them. If two of the corners are designated A and B, the lights appeared in the order ABAB a number of times and then shifted to BAAB. The subjects gave large orientation reactions to the A which occurred out of sequence, i.e. as a surprise. It is argued that novelty is eliminated here, since none of the stimuli in itself was novel at this stage of the experiment. It may be thought that some hair-splitting is involved here, however, since there was novelty in the change of sequence. The experiment may be taken to demonstrate that the mechanisms for stimulus analysis can detect novelty in the arrangement of patterns of stimuli as well as in the absolute properties of the stimulus.

(6) *Complexity, uncertainty, incongruity.* Complex figures elicit orientation reactions more readily than simple ones. For example, Berlyne (1958a) found that three to nine-month-old children presented with three oblongs of different geometric design and complexity looked first at the most complex one. Fantz (1958a, 1958b) found infant chimpanzees and humans preferred to look at a chessboard pattern rather than at a plain square. In adults orientation reactions are readily evoked by incongruous pictures such as that of an animal with a lion's body and an elephant's head (Berlyne, 1958b).

(7) *Conflict.* In conditioning situations the animal first makes orientation reactions to the novel situation. Then as the conditioning becomes well established and "automatic" the orientation reactions disappear. Now when discrimination learning is introduced the animal once more makes orientation reactions to both the positive and negative stimuli until the discrimination becomes perfect. Then the orientation reactions once again disappear (Bykov, 1958; Grastyan, 1959; Sokolov, 1960). When the positive and negative stimuli are very similar and an intermediate stimulus is presented, the orientation reaction is very strong. Pavlov assumed that this situation involves conflict and elicits strong oriention reactions on that account. This is of course the situation which is likely to lead to experimental neurosis.

Conflict in a situation where there is no perceptual discrimination difficulty has been isolated by Berlyne (1961) as a factor eliciting orientation reactions. In one experiment the subject was shown a diamond with two lights at each of the four corners. He was instructed that if two lights came on in one corner he was to move a lever towards that corner; if one light came on in one corner and another light simultaneously in another, he could move the lever towards either corner (but would presumably be in conflict). By this arrangement Berlyne has neatly controlled the variable of stimulus intensity, which remains the same in both situations. Subjects in the conflict situation gave significantly larger PGRs. In a similar experiment Berlyne (1961) has confirmed the importance of conflict using a word association test. This experiment rests on the work of Laffal in differentiating words which produce high and low certainties of response, the supposition being that some words produce low certainties of response because they are about equally associated with several response words. Here again low certainty response words elicited the large PGRs.

While Berlyne has made an important contribution in distinguishing these seven kinds of situation evoking orientation reactions, it seems likely that a gain in simplicity can be achieved by reducing them to three. The first is novelty. This includes Berlyne's variables of novelty, surprise (where there is something novel about the sequence of stimuli), and complexity – uncertainty – incongruity (where the novelty lies in the patterning of the stimuli). The second situation involves conflict. The third type of stimulus eliciting the orientation reaction is the stimulus which has special significance by virtue of the subject's previous conditioning: thus such stimuli as one's own name and "Look out" are not novel but continue to elicit the orientation reaction. Evidently, therefore, the normal mechanisms of blocking the orientation reaction to repeated stimuli are by-passed in the case of these conditioned stimuli which are of special significance to the subject. This is an inference that must be handled by theories of the physiological mechanisms of the orientation reaction, to which we now turn.

CHAPTER 2

PHYSIOLOGICAL MECHANISMS IN THE ORIENTATION REACTION

THE most comprehensive model for the orientation reaction is that advanced by Sokolov (Sokolov, 1960; Voronin and Sokolov, 1960). The model is shown in general form in Fig. 1 and in more detail for visual stimuli in Fig. 2.

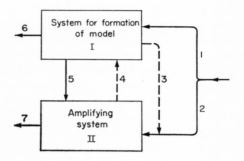

FIG. 1. Sokolov's model for the orientation reaction. I: modelling system. II: amplifying system. 1: specific pathway from sense organs to cortical level of modelling system. 2: collateral to reticular formation (represented here as amplifying device). 3: negative feedback from modelling system to synaptic connections between collaterals from specific pathway and reticular formation (RF) to block input in the case of habituated stimuli. 4: ascending activating influences from the RF to the modelling system (cortex). 5: pathway from modelling system to amplifying system (this is the pathway through which the impulses signifying non-concordance between input and existing neuronal models are transmitted from cortex to RF. 6: to specific responses caused by coincidence between the external stimulus and the neuronal model (habitual responses). 7: to the vegetative and somatic components arising from the stimulation of the RF. (From Sokolov, 1960.)

In general terms the theory proposes that the stimulus analysis takes place in the cortex; after analysis the cortex initiates excitation or inhibition of the orientation reaction. More specifically, the model can be broken down into a number of assumptions as follows:

14

1. Afferent stimulation passes up the classical sensory tracts to the cortex and also sends excitory impulses via the afferent collaterals into the reticular formation.

2. In the case of novel or significant stimuli the cortex sends down excitatory impulses to the reticular formation. Therefore the cortex acts as an analysing mechanism, determining whether the stimuli

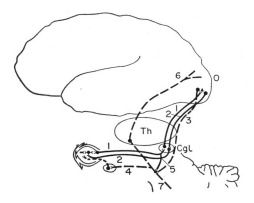

FIG. 2. Specific and non-specific pathways and their relationship to the visual analyser. Schema of relationship between the specific stimulation of the visual system and the participation of the reticular formation (RF) in the shift of excitation in the cortical and peripheral parts of the analyser. The RF could be excited either via collaterals, 5, or via non-specific descending corticoreticular pathways, 3. Cgl = lateral geniculate nucleus; Th = non-specific midline thalamus; O = occiput; 1 = specific pathway from retina to O; 2 = specific descending pathway from O through Cgl to retina; 3 = non-specific descending pathway from cortex to RF; 4= pathway from RF to sympathetic ganglion and retina; 5=collateral from the specific pathway leading into RF; 6 = non-specific ascending pathway from Th to O; and 7 = ascending and descending pathways in RF. (From Sokolov, 1960.)

are novel or significant. In developing this part of the theory, Sokolov advances the concept of the "nervous model". According to this conception, incoming stimuli leave traces of all their characteristics within the nervous system and especially in the cortex. These traces are the nervous models. They preserve information about the intensity and duration of the stimulus as well as other more obvious stimulus dimensions. To quote Sokolov's own description of this concept: "The model postulates a chain of neural cells which preserve information about the intensity, the quality, the duration, and the order of presentation of the stimuli" (Sokolov, 1960, p. 205).

Sokolov now assumes that any incoming stimulus is compared with the nervous models existing in the cortex. Two things may happen: (a) the stimulus may not match any existing nervous model; in this case the orientation reaction occurs; (b) the stimulus may match a nervous model; in this case the orientation reaction is blocked. This model does not of course explain the activation of the orientation reaction by familiar but significant stimuli.

3. The mechanism proposed for activation of the orientation reaction is twofold. First, non-specific stimulation via the collateral afferents activates the reticular formation. Second and more important, the cortex sends down excitatory impulses to the reticular formation. The activation of the reticular formation from both these sources, afferent collaterals and cortex, then initiates the orientation reaction.

4. If the incoming stimulus is a familiar one it matches a model in the cortex. In this case the cortex does not send excitatory impulses to the reticular formation and it blocks the excitatory non-specific effects via the afferent collaterals. These mechanisms of habituation form a somewhat different topic and will be left for discussion in Chapter 4.

It is evident that there are a number of assumptions in this theory which are more or less independent of each other and which can be examined separately. Two of the most important of these are discussed below.

The role of the reticular formation in the orientation reaction: few will be disposed to argue with Sokolov's assumption that the activation of the reticular formation is an important part in the chain of events giving rise to the orientation reaction. The classical experiments of Moruzzi and Magoun (1949) demonstrating the arousal reaction following stimulation of the reticular formation by implanted electrodes have been repeated many times. In the normal animal, the reticular formation is activated through the afferent collaterals. Apart from the gross behavioural signs of arousal and alerting, the autonomic and attention aspects of the orientation reaction are also present following reticular stimulation. As far as attention is concerned, the elicitation of the orientation reaction by stimulation from electrodes implanted in the hypothalamus and the reticular formation has been reported by Hess (1949) and Grastyan (1959). On examination of the histology, Grastyan found that all the points responsible for this effect were in the neighbourhood of the fornix system (this system conveys afferent impulses to and efferent impulses from the hippocampus). The orientation reaction obtained is of a very exaggerated kind, in which the cat appears riveted onto a moving object, so much so that it may lose its balance as the object shifts. The reaction, called by Grastyan the "sensory fixation reaction", is somewhat similar to Klüver's "hypermetamorphosis" following temporal lobectomy. Similar reactions follow destruction of the entorhinal area (Adey, Merrillees and Sunderland, 1956).

Stimulation of the reticular formation by implanted electrodes also reproduces the autonomic and EEG components of the orientation reaction. Further, the generalized and localized orientation reactions are elicited by stimulation of different parts of the reticular formation. Stimulation of the brain stem reticular formation elicits the generalized orientation reaction (Jasper, 1957; Sokolov, 1963a) or, according to Gastaut and Roger (1960), the startle – defensive reaction: these reactions are difficult to differentiate. Gastaut and Roger (1960) reports that the continuation of intense stimulation of the brain stem reticular formation is likely to produce fainting and that a similar mechanism is present in epilepsy.

Stimulation of the thalamic reticular formation elicits the localized orientation reaction, with EEG desynchronization in localized cortical areas and less intense autonomic reactions. The work of Hess (1949) and Gastaut et al. (1952) indicates that the localized orientation reaction is obtained best by stimulation of the intralaminar nuclei and the reticular nucleus.

A second important assumption in Sokolov's model is that the cortex, on analysing the stimulus as novel, sends excitatory impulses to the reticular formation. There is well-substantiated evidence that cortico – reticular connections of the kind postulated by Sokolov do exist and that stimulation of the cortex can elicit the orientation reaction via these pathways (French, 1957; Lagutina, 1955). The most important cortical areas from which connections to the reticular formation project are in the sensorimotor cortex, superior temporal gyrus and tip, paraoccipital region and entorhinal cortex.

Lagutina has produced a localization map, shown in Fig. 3, which indicates the points at which the orientation reactions can be elicited by stimulation through implanted electrodes. This map is based on experiments on 28 cats and 4 apes. The animals were moving freely and both autonomic and behavioural orientation reactions were elicited by stimulation of these points.

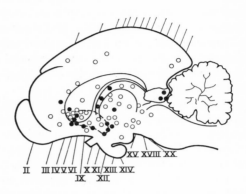

FIG. 3. Lagutina's localization map of orientation reactions elicited by stimulation through implanted electrodes. Dots indicate stimulation points eliciting generalized orientation reactions; circles, points eliciting localized orientation reactions.

Somewhat similar results have been reported by French (1957) using monkeys. Moderately intense stimulation of cortical areas projecting to the reticular formation elicited orientation reactions in the monkeys, with the animals searching around as if seeking the source of this novel form of stimulation. More intense stimulation elicits the startle – defensive reaction, with the animal cringing in the corner of the cage, or, with yet more intense stimulation, racing about the cage in a frenzy of terror. Stimulation of these cortical areas also elicits the autonomic and EEG components of the orientation reaction. Hence, although it does not follow that these cortico – reticular connections are activated when an animal makes an orientation reaction, it is certainly plausible that they convey excitatory impulses to the reticular formation in the manner suggested by Sokolov.

Additional evidence of a different kind in favour of Sokolov's model is provided by Thompson and Welker (1963), who showed that cats give poor orientation reactions to sound after bilateral ablations of the auditory cortex. Where an intact cat will give rapid, immediate and accurate orientation towards the source of the sound in one movement, ablated cats tended to give delayed and poorly executed movements. A similar result was reported by Bremer (1954). These observations support Sokolov's supposition that the cortex plays an active role in mobilizing the orientation reaction.

Another consideration in favour of this theory is the subtlety of the discriminations which can elicit the orientation reaction. When the subject is habituated to a group of words of similar meaning, for example, an orientation reaction is elicited by a word of different meaning. It is difficult to believe that stimulus analysis of this subtlety can take place anywhere but in the cortex. Evidently, therefore, the cortex analyses the stimulus as novel and sets in train excitatory impulses to the reticular formation which energizes the orientation reaction.

THE FALL IN SENSORY THRESHOLDS

It is likely that three mechanisms are operative in the fall in sensory thresholds that accompanies the orientation reaction. First, there is an increase in the excitability of the whole cortex (in the generalized orientation reaction) or in the part of the cortex involved in the discrimination (in the localized orientation reaction). Secondly, there is direct neural stimulation of the receptors and afferent relays through descending pathways from the reticular formation and from the cortex. The third mechanism is indirect and involves a change in the blood supply of the cortex and of the receptors, which increases their excitability.

1. The increase in the excitation of the cortex is manifested in three ways.

A. There is an increase in the frequency of the EEG rhythms. It appears likely that the EEG desynchronization is in some way related to an increase in the efficiency of the cortex. The most striking indication of this relationship is probably the experiment of Lansing, Schwartz and Lindsley (1959) on the effects of a warning signal on reaction times. It is well known that the presentation of a warning signal just before the test stimulus shortens the reaction time quite considerably. What Lansing *et al.* demonstrate is that the warning signal only has this facilitatory effect if it is presented in time to produce alpha blocking; warning signals presented about 100 msec or less before the test stimulus are too late to produce alpha blocking and do not facilitate the reaction time; warning signals presented between about 100 and 400 msec before the test stimulus produce some alpha blocking and some facilitation, while warning signals presented over about 400 msec before the test stimulus produce the full amount of alpha blocking and of facilitation of the reaction time. Figure 4 shows this relationship. Since input and output times in a visual reaction time are fairly constant, the reduction in reaction time is most probably due to an increase in the efficiency of the cortex, of which the alpha blocking appears to be an index.

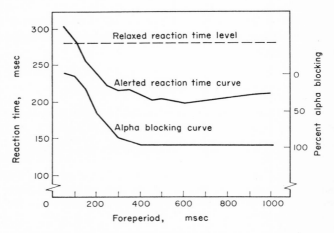

FIG. 4. Reaction time and alpha blocking plotted as a function of the foreperiod interval. Note that the reaction time is reduced to a minimum when the foreperiod ranges from 300 to 1000 msec, and that the *alpha-blocking curve* follows a similar time course. Once activation occurs there is no further reduction of the reaction time. Relaxed unalerted reaction time, 280 msec; alerted reaction time, minimum 206 msec. (From Lansing *et al.*, 1959.)

B. A second indication of the heightened excitability of the cortex is Lindsley's (1958) finding that a pair of light flashes 50 msec apart normally produce a single evoked potential in the visual cortex of the cat. After reticular stimulation the two flashes produce two evoked potentials. Stimulation of the mesencephalic reticular formation also produces larger evoked potentials in the lateral geniculate bodies (Bremer and Stoupel, 1959; Dumont and Dell, 1958). These experiments show the increased discriminatory power of the cortex and the sensory system under reticular stimulation, such as occurs during the orientation reaction.

C. To these two indications of increased cortical excitation Sokolov has added a third, namely the threshold of photic driving of the EEG rhythm. Sokolov's results are shown in Fig. 5. Here

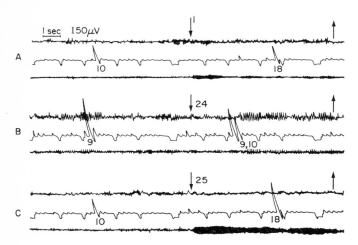

Fig. 5. Change of response of visual cortex to 18/sec flicker after habituation and external stimulation. In (A), (B), and (C), from top to bottom: occipital EEG, frequency analysis of EEG, and response of the 18 cps filter of analyser. (A) Before flicker, EEG frequency was 10 cps. 1st presentation evoked EEG response at 18 cps, seen most precisely on the 18 cps filter. (B) 24th presentation (habituation): alpha rhythm has slowed to 9 cps. Flicker produces slight increase in frequency (i.e., 10 cps peak in analyser trace), but no response at 18 cps. (C) 25th presentation after auditory stimulation: alpha rhythm drops in amplitude. Same flicker at 18/sec now produces strong driving with complete depression of alpha rhythm. The 18 cps filter reacts intensely. (From Sokolov, 1960.)

the subject has an alpha rhythm of 10 cps, determined by the Gray Walter analyser. The subject is then stimulated by an 18 cps flickering light; this stimulus evokes the orientation reaction and drives the EEG rhythm at the same 18 cps frequency. After twenty-three presentations the same 18 cps flicker was incapable of producing photic driving and the alpha rhythm has declined from 10 to 9 cps.

This is of course habituation of the orientation reaction and, Sokolov argues, indicates the diminished responsiveness of the visual cortex. A disinhibiting stimulus (a tone 70 db above threshold) produces an orientation reaction, increases the excitability of the cortex and restores the photic driving to the 18 cps flicker.

2. The receptors are also made more sensitive by neural impulses from the reticular formation and the cortex. The feedback paths from the cortex have been isolated by the Russian workers Poliakov (1959) and Shlolkin-Iarros (1958) and the paths from the reticular formation by Granit (1955), who has shown that excitation of the reticular formation increases the excitability of the sense organs.

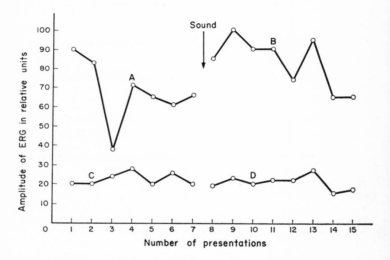

FIG. 6. During presentation of flicker, flicker response of ERG decreases. B wave at onset of light is not changed. After administration of sound, flicker response of the ERG increases. B wave does not change. (A) Amplitude of flicker response of ERG. (B) Amplitude of flicker response of ERG after orienting by a sound stimulus (note increase). (C) Amplitude of B wave of ERG. (D) Amplitude of B wave of ERG after orienting by a sound stimulus (no change). (From Sokolov, 1960.)

An experiment of Sokolov (1960) is designed to show that this mechanism is operative during the orientation reaction. In this experiment the responses of the rabbit were studied by means of a special contact lens which is inserted into the eye; around this lens there is a ring which prevents the eyes from closing. The object of this is to eliminate the interfering effect of changes in the transmission of light between the lids during stimulation. The pupils are dilated by administration of atropine. The electroretinogram (ERG) is recorded by the Gray Walter analyser. The effects of the orientation reaction are shown in Fig. 6. The stimulus is flashes of light at 20 cps; presentation of sound, evoking the orientation reaction, increases the response. Under the influence of the orientation reaction, the shape of the ERG is also changed so that the highest point comes nearer to the onset of each flash.

Confirmatory evidence for the increase of sensitivity in the peripheral pathways during stimulation has been reported by Chang (1960). He showed that if the visual system is stimulated by a light, there is an increase in the response to direct electrical stimulation of the geniculate body. This indicates facilitation in the visual pathway. Steady illumination of the visual system also increases auditory evoked responses evoked by electrical stimulation of the medial geniculate.

3. A third mechanism is proposed by Sokolov for the increase in sensitivity during the orientation reaction. This is an indirect humoral factor. This assumption is based on the work of Jacobson and Gestring (1958) showing the existence of humoral factors affecting the ERG in cats. The mechanisms for these influences are not at present clear and it is regarded by the Russian workers as a possibility for future investigation.

CHAPTER 3

THE HABITUATION OF THE ORIENTATION REACTION

WHEN a stimulus is presented again and again the orientation reaction gets progressively weaker and eventually disappears. This is the phenomenon of habituation. The animal may appear to take no further notice of the stimulus, or the orientation reaction may give way to some other kind of reaction. These facts give rise to a large number of interesting problems. In this chapter the chief facts involved are summarized, and in the next there is a consideration of the theories that have been put forward.

With repeated presentation of the stimulus there are three possible effects: (a) an adaptive reflex may occur to certain kinds of stimuli; (b) intense stimuli will produce a defensive reflex; or (c) eventually no response at all occurs.

For example, in the case of stimulation with flashes of light, the initial orientation reaction includes dilation of the pupil; but with repeated stimulation this reaction gives way to pupil contraction. Here the orientation reaction is habituated and replaced by an adaptive reaction. With more intense stimuli, such as repeated electric shock, the orientation reaction gives way to the defensive reaction. The speed with which a defensive reaction is obtained is a function both of the intensity of the stimulus and of the number of presentations.

THE COURSE OF HABITUATION OF THE ORIENTATION REACTION

Of these various effects we are concerned here with habituation such as is obtained with repeated stimulation by stimuli of moderate intensity. Sokolov (1963a) distinguishes a number of stages in the development of habituation:

1. The generalized orientation reaction (Sokolov) or tonic orientation reaction (Sharpless and Jasper, 1956): characterized by EEG activation over the whole cortex, the PGR, pupil dilation, a pause in respiration, muscle tension and head movements towards

the stimulus. Typically this reaction is obtained with decreasing intensity for something like 10–15 stimulations, depending on the intensity of the stimulus and other stimulus variables. According to both Sharpless and Jasper and Sokolov, this generalized orientation reaction is comparatively lengthy, lasting from a few seconds to many minutes (when a drowsy animal is woken up, for example), has a long latent period of up to 30 sec, is rapidly habituated, and recovers slowly over a period of hours or days.

2. The localized orientation reaction (Sokolov), or phasic orientation reaction (Sharpless and Jasper), now remains. This consists of an EEG reaction in the cortical area of the particular sense organ being stimulated. This reaction takes longer to habituate and will typically survive for something of the order of 25–30 stimulations. Sharpless and Jasper describe this reaction as differing from the generalized orientation reaction in several respects: it is short, generally disappearing within 10–15 sec after the end of the stimulus, it has a short latency, is very resistant to habituation, and recovers within a few minutes. Thus Sokolov and Sharpless and Jasper are in agreement in finding that the generalized orientation reaction habituates more quickly than the localized orientation reaction.

3. The subject becomes drowsy and at the same time the EEG alpha rhythm is replaced by slow large amplitude waves. EEG desynchronization is typically the last response to disappear.

4. The subject is still drowsy. The generalized orientation reaction now returns. This paradoxical fact receives some confirmation from Oswald's (1962, p. 106) results: here also the return of the PGR was observed, but in these experiments this did not occur until the subject was in medium depth sleep.

5. The stage of secondary habituation now begins and occurs in the same order as in the first stage of habituation, i.e. the generalized orientation reaction again gives way to the localized orientation reaction and the local EEG reaction is the last to survive. However, secondary habituation takes longer than primary habituation and will generally take something of the order of twice as many or even dozens of stimulations before habituation is complete. During this stage the alerting of the subject, such as by giving him a task, results in the disappearance of the secondary orientation reaction (Sokolov, 1963a, pp. 121–122).

6. The subject eventually goes to sleep. There has been some

C

dispute about whether the repetition of a stimulus gives rise to sleep or whether the subject might have gone to sleep just as easily without the monotonous stimulation. Pavlov maintained the first possibility, assuming that the repetitive stimulus generates inhibition in the cerebral cortex, and that the inhibition irradiates over the cortex and then to the subcortex, inducing sleep. But Konorski (1948) argues that experimental dogs placed in the stand without any stimulation go to sleep just as quickly and points out that in human beings monotonous stimulation, such as a brightly illuminated room, to which we have long since extinguished our orientation reaction, hinders us from going to sleep. Consequently Konorski argues that Pavlov was incorrect in assuming that habituation of the orientation reaction leads to sleep.

Subsequent experiments have tended to favour Pavlov rather than Konorski on this issue. For example, Gastaut and Bert (1961) report an experiment in which 156 normal adults were given repetitive stimulation for a period of 8 min. Of the 102 subjects who had alpha rhythms, 45 developed EEG sleep rhythms during the repetitive stimulation and many subjects were definitely asleep. It is obvious that these adults would not have gone to sleep during this 8-min period if they had simply been sitting in a chair. Somewhat similar results have been reported by Oswald (1962). Moruzzi (1960) also reports the very rapid development of sleep in animals during habituation and extinction experiments.

VARIABLES AFFECTING HABITUATION

1. *Stimulus Variables*

Stimulus intensity. Habituation rates are generally more rapid with low intensity stimuli. There is, however, an exception to this in that threshold stimuli are very resistant to habituation (Sokolov, 1963a). For example, threshold stimuli continue to elicit EEG desynchronization after hundreds of presentations (Mihalevskaya, 1958). This finding was not obtained by Bradley (1957), who reports very rapid habituation in 4–5 trials with threshold stimuli. However, the Russian workers are very experienced in this matter and their findings are probably best accepted. The reason for failure of habituation of threshold stimuli is probably that they form a special case of difficult discriminations, all of which reactivate the orientation reaction and do not habituate.

An experiment of Sokolov exemplifies the effects of stimulus intensity on the vascular component of the orientation reaction (vasodilation in the head, vasoconstriction in the limbs). The results are shown in Fig. 7. There are strong orientation reactions to the auditory stimulus at threshold, and again at high intensities.

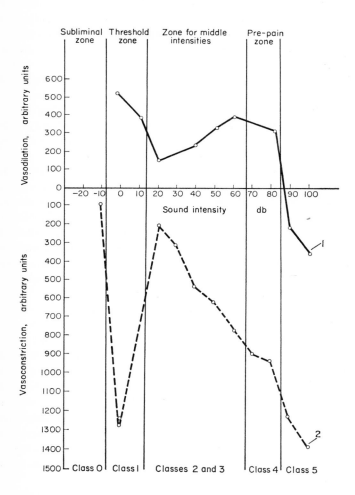

FIG. 7. Relationship between vascular reactions and the assessed strengths of a strong acoustic stimulus. 1: vascular reactions in the head region. 2: vascular reactions in the hand. (From Sokolov, 1963a.)

Duration of the stimulus. A very brief stimulus either produces no reaction or the reaction is quickly habituated. Very long stimuli also habituate quickly, leaving stimuli of intermediate duration as the most difficult to habituate (Sokolov, 1963a, p. 119).

Difficult discriminations. These delay habituation in cases where the subject has to make a positive reaction to one stimulus and a negative reaction to another and the stimuli are difficult to discriminate. If there is considerable difficulty in discrimination, the orientation reaction to both stimuli can still occur after hundreds of trials (Sokolov, 1963a).

Time intervals. The shorter the intervals between the stimuli, the quicker the habituation (Bradley, 1957; Gastaut and Bert, 1961).

Spontaneous recovery. After the elapse of time following habituation, the orientation reaction shows some partial recovery, which lessens with further habituation until eventually the orientation reaction is completely and permanently habituated.

Gastaut and Bert (1961) report an experiment in which human beings were habituated once a week to auditory and visual stimuli, the alpha–blocking reaction being taken as the index of habituation. In these conditions they found that habituation of the alpha blocking and the appearance of sleep records was speeded up as the weeks went by, until after a few weeks alpha blocking disappeared at the first stimulus. The resting EEG activity of the subjects also changed in the direction of a lower frequency of alpha rhythm, presumably a reflection of habituation to the experimental situation.

Disinhibition. After a stimulus has been habituated, a strong extraneous stimulus restores the orientation reaction. The effect was observed by Pavlov and has been confirmed by many other investigators, e.g. by Prosser and Hunter (1936) in rats. But after several successive applications, the disinhibitory effect disappears (Sokolov, 1963a). Sharpless and Jasper (1956) observed that the disinhibitory stimulus only has its effect if the habituated stimulus occurs simultaneously or very soon afterwards. They argue that this indicates that the disinhibiting stimulus does not dissipate the inhibition and that more probably the orientation reaction is restored by the momentary increase in arousal brought about by the novel stimulus.

Generalization. The specificity of habituation of the orientation reaction is not absolute but involves a certain amount of generalization. A number of detailed results on the generalization of habituation of EEG arousal to tones in the cat have been reported by Apelbaum and his collaborators (Apelbaum, Silva, and Frick, 1959). A cat primarily habituated to a tone of 200 cps does not respond to tones up to 220 cps, but begins to respond to 230–500 cps. Further, after habituation to a tone of one frequency, habituation to tones of similar frequencies is facilitated. Similarly, Beck, Doty and Kwi (1958) found that animals habituated to one stimulus habituate more readily to other stimuli. Caspers, Lerche and Grüter (1958) found that there was more generalization in rats when they were asleep than when they were awake. In spite of these findings there is also evidence in favour of Sharpless and Jasper's (1956) conclusion that habituation is fairly specific to the stimulus. There is no doubt that after complete habituation to one stimulus an orientation reaction can frequently be obtained to other stimuli (Roger, Voronin and Sokolov, 1958; Glickman and Feldman, 1960).

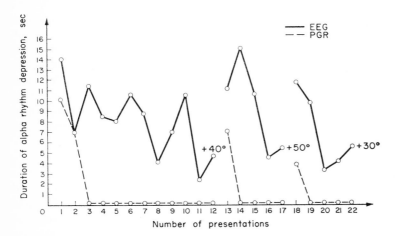

FIG. 8. Habituation of alpha rhythm and PGR to stimulation by a light spot focused on a point on the horizontal meridian of the projection perimeter on the nasal part of the retina. After 2nd presentation, the generalized reaction is completely inhibited. The localized orienting reaction (alpha depression) is diminished only. A change of position from 40° to 50° (from the central fixation point) evokes generalized reaction (PGR and increased duration of alpha rhythm depression). Repetition of the same stimulation evokes decrease in local orienting reflex and complete disappearance of generalized orienting reaction. Change to 30° produces, again, a generalized response and increase of the alpha rhythm depression. Habitation is specific to the point of retina stimulated. (From Sokolov, 1960.)

In human beings the degree of generalization of habituation can be seen in the following experiment of Sokolov (1960). Here the subject is presented with a very small light focused on a point 40° to the nasal side of the retina. The PGR and alpha rhythm depression were recorded. Figure 8 shows the results of repeated stimulation at 40-sec intervals. On the 13th and 18th trials the stimulus is moved to stimulate different parts of the retina. The orientation reaction revives, but is not so strong as to the original stimulus and it habituates more quickly to the generalized stimulus.

Conditioned (*signal*) *stimuli.* Normally a repeated stimulus is habituated. If, however, the subject learns that the stimulus has particular significance for him (that is to say, the stimulus becomes a conditioned or signal stimulus), then habituation is very greatly prolonged or never occurs. Familiar everyday examples of this are such things as the continued orientation reactions people give to hearing their own names, to stimuli which are particularly important for them such as infants' cries for mothers, and for words which herald important events such as "Watch out", etc.

At a more experimental level, a habituated stimulus can be made into a conditioned stimulus either by pairing it with shock or in man simply by telling the subject to pay attention to it. Both these courses restore the orientation reaction. In a situation where the subject is required to make a response to the stimulus, the orientation reaction eventually habituates when the response becomes fully automatic but this typically takes several hundreds of trials.

2. *Subject Variables*

Cortical injury and ablation. Destruction of the cerebral cortex lengthens habituation of the orientation reaction very considerably and, with total ablation, may make habituation impossible. The effect was observed in Pavlov's laboratories by Zeliony (quoted by Pavlov, 1927, p. 310) in dogs and has frequently been observed since. Difficulties in habituating the orientation reaction in human beings with cortical damage have also been found (Briullova, 1958) and the same is true of children with defective cortical functioning such as premature and hydrocephalic infants (Bronstein, Itina, Kamenetskaya, and Sytova, 1958).

Similar results have been reported outside Russian laboratories, for example by Jouvet (1961), who found that in chronic decerebrated cats it was impossible to habituate the orientation reaction after as many as 800 stimuli. Cats with ablation of neocortex but with paleocortex intact were also unable to habituate. With partial decortication, habituation was shown in direct proportion to the amount of brain extirpation. Grastyan (1959, p. 263) reports similar results.

On the other hand, discrepant findings are reported by Sharpless and Jasper (1956), who found that cats with ablation of the auditory cortex were able to habituate to specific tones as quickly as normals. Sokolov's associate, Vinogradova, in seeking to explain this puzzling discrepancy, has suggested that some auditory cortex may have remained after the operation and that this would be sufficient to account for the habituation (Vinogradova, 1961). But even if this explanation is correct, some slowing of the habituation rate would be expected. However, taking the evidence as a whole, Sharpless and Jasper's finding must be regarded as an exception and the weight of the evidence lies in favour of Pavlov's original conclusion that decortication greatly delays habituation of the orientation reaction.

Phylogenetic differences. Vinogradova (1961) reports a number of Russian studies showing that habituation is quicker in animals higher in the phylogenetic scale. The same conclusion is reached by Gastaut and Bert (1961) from work on habituation of blocking of the alpha rhythm: for a stimulus requiring 3–4 presentations for habituation in man, 6–7 presentations are required in (unspecified) animals.

Individual differences. The following have been found deficient in habituation:

1. Old people suffering from senile dementia (Kazmiin and Fedorov, 1951).
2. Certain schizophrenics (for review, see Lynn, 1963).
3. Certain neurotics (Sokolov, 1963a, p. 122).
4. Dog subjects with "weak" nervous systems (Vinogradov, 1933).
5. Human subjects with "strong excitatory potentials" (this variable is discussed in Chapter 7).

3. *Drug Effects*

There has been rather little research on the effects of drugs on the orientation reaction. Some work has been done with chlororomazine. Rothballer (1955) reported that it abolishes or reduces the generalized orientation reaction but has no effect on the localized orientation reaction. Anokhin (1958) has reported similar results after administration of chlorpromazine to rabbits; it is also impossible to get disinhibition effects after the administration of chlorpromazine. Jus and Jus (1960) administered chlorpromazine to 20 human adults and also found that the generalized orientation reaction was abolished, leaving the localized orientation reaction unimpaired. Indeed, these authors report that after chlorpromazine has been taken the localized orientation reaction is *enhanced* and a habituated stimulus once more elicits the phasic EEG reaction.

These facts support the hypothesis put forward by several writers (e.g. Jasper, 1957; Gastaut and Roger, 1960) that there are two distinct anatomical sites for the generalized and localized orientation reactions. Further, the fact that chlorpromazine appears to depress only the brain stem reticular formation and leaves the thalamic reticular formation unimpaired (Jasper, 1957) favours the assumption that the brain stem reticular formation mediates the generalized orientation reaction and the thalamic reticular formation the localized orientation reaction. The enhanced and dishabituated phasic reactions following chlorpromazine reported by Jus and Jus suggests the existence of an active inhibitory mechanism in the brain stem reticular formation.

The effects of another depressant, carisaprodol,* on the PGR component of the orientation reaction has been reported by Lynn and Eysenck (1963). Thirty subjects were tested in three conditions: after dosage with 350 mg carisaprodol, after placebo, and with no drug. The subjects were presented with auditory stimulation until the orientation reaction was no longer elicited. There was some tendency for the subjects to habituate more rapidly after dosage with carisaprodol.

Since the orientation reaction is reduced and habituated more quickly by depressants it may be inferred that it will be increased and habituated more slowly by stimulants. Key and Bradley (1960) have confirmed this expectation using LSD. There are also a number of Russian reports on schizophrenics showing that administration of caffeine increases the size and stability of the orientation reaction (e.g. Gamburg, 1958; Streltsova, 1958).

* A derivative of meprobamate.

CHAPTER 4

NEUROLOGICAL MODELS FOR HABITUATION OF THE ORIENTATION REACTION

WE NOW turn to a consideration of the numerous neurological models of the habituation process. Initially, we have divided these into "one-stage models" and "two-stage models". One-stage models are those that assume that when a particular body of neurones is continually stimulated an inhibitory process is generated in these neurones which raises their threshold of response and eventually eliminates the response entirely. The generation of inhibition is responsible for the diminution and eventual habituation of the orientation reaction. Although different investigators have proposed different anatomical sites for the generation of this inhibitory process they have in common this assumption of a fatigue-like process in the neurones which receive the stimuli and by virtue of this "one-stage" assumption they are equally untenable. The most prominent theories of this type are those of Pavlov, Sharpless and Jasper, Gastaut and Roitbak.

PAVLOV

The first important investigator to put forward a one-stage theory was Pavlov (1927). His theory assumed that with repeated stimulation the cortical neurones of the analyser become exhausted. This exhaustion is accompanied by the generation of a "special process or substance which prevents it from responding". This is internal inhibition. The orientation reaction now ceases. With further repetition of the stimulus, internal inhibition spreads to neighbouring neurones, to the whole of the cerebral cortex and then to the subcortex: this causes the animal to become drowsy and then go to sleep.

There are several grounds for rejecting this theory.

1. If a subject is habituated to a stimulus of a given intensity, the orientation reaction is restored by a stimulus of the same quality

33

but of weaker intensity (Sokolov, 1960). This shows that habituation is not simply a matter of higher thresholds of neurones resulting from a fatigue-like inhibitory process.

2. If the subject is habituated to a stimulus of a particular duration of time and is then presented with a stimulus exactly the same except that it is shorter, an orientation reaction occurs after the end of the stimulus, i.e. at the point at which it is recognizably different from the habituated stimulus. Some of these effects are shown in Fig. 9. This again shows that habituation is not simply a fatigue-like process.

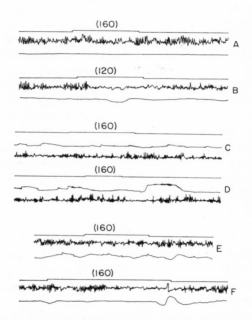

FIG. 9. Reappearance of orienting reflex on diminishing intensity of the light stimulation. In (A) to (F), from top to bottom: signal of light in relative units, occipital EEG, and PGR. (A) After three sessions, complete habituation. (B) Diminishing light intensity from 160 to 120 relative units evokes a generalized reaction (alpha depression and PGR). (C) Habituation to 160 relative units of intensity with a duration of 5 sec. (D) Decrease in duration evokes the orientation reaction at the moment when the light is cut short. (E) Habituation to 160 relative units and a duration of 5 sec. (F) Prolongation of the same intensity evokes the orientation reaction at the moment when the duration exceeds that of the standard stimulation. (From Sokolov, 1960.)

3. Transforming the habituated stimulus into a conditioned stimulus (such as by asking the subject to respond to it or pairing it with an unconditioned stimulus) immediately restores the orientation reaction. This again argues against the assumption of the generation of inhibition in the neurones responsible for analysis of the stimulus.

4. A subject can be habituated to the simultaneous presentation of two tones, e.g. of 70 and 90 db, and the presentation of one of them will then reactivate the orientation reaction.

5. Habituated stimuli continue to elicit evoked potentials in the cerebral cortex (Sharpless and Jasper, 1956). This indicates that the cortex is not itself inhibited during habituation and that the inhibitory block must be occurring elsewhere.

6. The spontaneous revival of the orientation reaction after its initial habituation and with continuous stimulation (as shown by Sokolov, see Chapter 3) cannot readily be explained by Pavlov's cortical inhibition theory.

For these reasons Pavlov's theory is unsatisfactory and has been rejected by most of his successors in Russia. The facts have driven several theorists to the adoption of two-stage theories, embodying the assumptions that there is an initial stage of stimulus analysis, followed by a second stage of activation or blocking of the orientation reaction. But before turning to these, we will review briefly some other one-stage theories which have recently been proposed by prominent neurophysiologists. They are essentially variations of Pavlov and suffer from the same difficulties.

SHARPLESS AND JASPER

The habituation model of Sharpless and Jasper (1956) has been advanced on the basis of work with sleeping cats. The cats were largely experimented upon while asleep in order to deal with the difficult problem of securing a constant level of electrical activity against which to assess the effects of stimulation. The habituation model put forward by Sharpless and Jasper embodies three principal assumptions.

1. Different levels of the nervous system are responsible for selective habituation with different degrees of sensitivity of discrimination. In the cat, Sharpless and Jasper found that the cerebral cortex appears to be responsible for selective pattern discrimination

and habituation. Thus normal cats can habituate a series of tones played in an ascending order and then give an orientation reaction to the same series played in a descending order. This selective habituation is abolished by ablation of the cortical auditory areas. These operated cats, however, are still capable of selective specific frequency habituation, presumably dealt with at the thalamic level. Section of the afferent pathway at the inferior colliculus, i.e. below the thalamic pathway, leaves the animal with only the brain stem analysing mechanisms. The animals are now capable of only very gross differentiation between stimuli of different sense modalities.

2. It is generally agreed that the ascending reticular activating system can be divided into two sections, the brain stem activating system and the thalamic activating system. Sharpless and Jasper propose that these are respectively responsible for the generalized (tonic) orientation reaction and the localized (phasic) orientation reaction. The generalized orientation reaction can be long lasting; thus a strong stimulus applied to a drowsy person (such as a telephone ringing in the middle of the night) can arouse him for an hour or so. The generalized orientation reaction also habituates quickly and remains habituated for a period of hours or days. The thalamic activating system habituates slowly, accounting for the slower habituation of the localized orientation reaction, and recovers quickly, within a few minutes. This is undoubtedly a simple and straightforward model to account for the different habituation rates of the generalized and localized orientation reactions. The location of these two orientation reactions in the brain stem reticular formation and the thalamic reticular formation respectively is well supported (see Chapter 2) and it is simple and plausible to assume different habituation rates.

3. Sharpless and Jasper also offer a novel explanation of disinhibition ("dehabituation"), the revival of a habituated orientation reaction by a novel stimulus. The effect was ascribed by Pavlov to dissipation of internal inhibition. The explanation put forward by Sharpless and Jasper is that the effect takes place because of the increase of arousal brought about by the novel stimulus. They tested the two hypotheses by varying the time intervals between presentation of the novel stimulus and the habituated stimulus. The results were that when the habituated stimulus was presented just after the novel stimulus, an orientation reaction was obtained (dehabituation); but if the arousal effects of the novel stimulus were

allowed to wear off, the old stimulus no longer elicited the orientation reaction. The second result is contrary to Pavlov's theory, since if a novel stimulus produces disinhibition by dissipating inhibition the time interval should make no difference to the disinhibition effect.

Apart from the experiment on disinhibition, the Sharpless and Jasper model of different loci for the generalized and localized orientation reactions, with different habituation rates, handles some of the evidence well:

1. It explains the different habituation rates of the generalized and localized orientation reactions.

2. Cutting the auditory tracts at the level of the inferior colliculus eliminates input into the thalamic activating system. Animals operated in this way show the expected result of retaining only the generalized orientation reaction and habituating very quickly, in a matter of two or three trials.

3. Moruzzi (1960) found that transection of the cat's brain at the upper pontine level abolished the generalized (tonic) orientation reaction, but the localized (phasic) EEG desynchronization was preserved. This evidence accords well with Sharpless and Jasper's hypotheses and suggests the localization of the generalized orientation reaction in the activating system of the upper part of the pons.

4. Further confirmation comes from Jus and Jus (1960). These workers injected twenty normal adult human beings with chloropromazine; when the chloropromazine depressed the brain stem it abolished generalized (tonic) alpha blocking but the localized reaction was retained.

On the other hand, there are difficulties in the Sharpless and Jasper model:

1. Cortical ablation of the specific sensory areas should have no effect on generalized or localized orientation reaction habituation rates. Although Sharpless and Jasper obtained this result there is a strong body of evidence showing that cortical injury delays habituation (see Chapter 3). This cannot be explained by the Sharpless and Jasper model.

2. Lesions in the brain stem activating system should abolish the generalized orientation reaction but leave the localized orientation reaction and its habituation intact. The facts appear to be that lesions of this kind placed in the mesencephalic pontine reticular

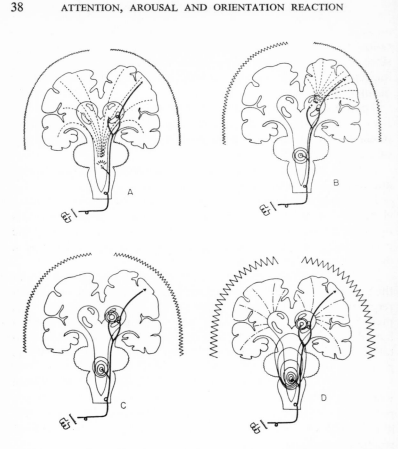

FIG. 10. Gastaut's model for habituation of the orientation reaction. A. A novel stimulus first evokes a startle–defensive reaction or generalized orientation reaction. Both the brain stem reticular formation and the thalamic reticular formation are activated, producing EEG desynchronization over the entire cortex. B. After some repetitions the stimulus only evokes the localized orientation reaction. Inhibition (represented by circles) has been generated in the brain stem reticular formation, but not yet in the thalamic reticular formation, which continues to produce EEG activation in the cortical analyser of the stimulus. C. With further repetition the orientation reaction is totally habituated. Inhibition (represented by concentric circles) is now present in the thalamic reticular formation as well as in the brain stem reticular formation. D. Further repetitions of the stimulus induce drowsiness and sleep, with large amplitude low frequency EEG rhythms. The stimulation has produced more inhibition in the reticular formation and this has reduced the level of activation in the cortex. (From Gastaut and Roger, 1960.)

formation bring about dehabituation and total failure of subsequent habituation (Hernández-Peón, 1960). These facts seem to imply that some rather fundamental inhibitory system located in the brain stem has been destroyed and its effect on abolishing habituation in the thalamic activating system cannot be explained by the Sharpless and Jasper model.

3. This model cannot explain the secondary orientation reaction after initial habituation, or recovery of the orientation reaction with drowsiness.

4. Finally, it suffers from the various difficulties discussed in connection with Pavlov's theory, which make any one-stage theory of habituation untenable.

GASTAUT

Gastaut (1957) has directed his attention mainly to the different rates of habituation of the generalized and the localized orientation reaction. The model he proposes is shown in Fig. 10, and the suggested stages in habituation are as follows.

1. A new, intense or significant stimulus first activates the whole reticular substance, and in particular the mesencephalic tegmentum; this activation produces the various manifestations of the orientation reaction and in particular generalized cortical desynchronization of the EEG (Fig. 10A).

2. With repeated presentation the stimulus generates inhibition (represented by circles in Fig. 10) in the mesencephalic reticular formation, but it continues to act on the thalamic reticular formation; activation of the thalamic reticular formation elicits the localized orientation reaction in the analyser of the sense organ being stimulated (Fig. 10B). This part of the theory is supported by experiments showing that stimulation of the thalamic reticular formation produces localized EEG desynchronization.

3. With further stimulation inhibition is generated in the thalamus too and the stimulus now produces no response (Fig. 10C). With still more repetition of the stimulus the inhibition continues to accumulate, eventually producing sleep.

It will be observed that Gastaut's model is very similar to that of Sharpless and Jasper and consequently has rather the same merits and limitations.

ROITBAK

Roitbak (1960) proposes that inhibition is generated in the non-specific thalamic reticular system. The brain stem reticular system is allotted its generally recognized activating function. Roitbak's model is shown in Fig. 11. With a single presentation of a stimulus,

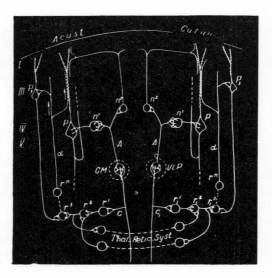

FIG. 11. Roitbak's habituation model. With repeated stimulation excitation breaks through r^2—r^1 . . . r^n and conveys inhibitory influences to the cortical analyser.

the impulses are relayed through the specific nuclei of the thalamus and thence to the cortex. They pass also into the non-specific thalamic nuclei, and here Roitbak assumes that transmission is difficult and a single stimulation has no further effect. However, when the stimulus is repeated it gradually breaks through the non-specific nuclei (r^1—r^2—r^3 . . . r^n in Fig. 11) and eventually sends inhibitory impulses to the cortical analyser. With further stimulation, the inhibition spreads, thereby causing reduced responsiveness to similar stimuli, and finally inducing sleep.

Roitbak cites a number of facts in favour of his theory. First, the slow EEG waves which accompany habituation of the orientation reaction may be caused by impulses from the non-specific thalamic reticular system. The evidence for this view is:

1. Electrical stimulation of the thalamic reticular system reproduces several features of the appearance of slow waves in the cortex, viz. in both cases the latency of about 30 msec following the stimulation is the same; the waves reach their maximum after about four stimulations; there is waxing and waning of the slow waves; with repetitive stimulation the waves develop more quickly; finally peripheral stimulation or stimulation of the brain stem reticular formation abolishes both the slow cortical waves and the recruiting responses evoked by stimulation of the thalamic reticular system (TRS).

2. Stimulation of the TRS which evokes a recruiting response in the cortex at the same time inhibits motor responses evoked by the stimulation of the motor area of the cortex (Grastyan *et al.*, 1954, 1955). There is also inhibition of the locomotor movements induced by the stimulation of the subcortical structures or occurring spontaneously (Grossman and Wang, 1956).

3. Electrical stimulation of the TRS can cause the onset of sleep (Hess, 1954; Akert *et al.*, 1952; Jung, 1957).

In essence Roitbak has taken the thalamo – cortical inhibitory system of Morison and Dempsey (1942) and Hess (1944) and assumed that this system is directly responsible for habituation. However, while the existence of this system has been fairly widely confirmed and accepted (Tissot and Monnier, 1961; Magoun, 1963), it is doubtful whether it can mediate habituation in the manner suggested by Roitbak. A crucial objection must be that selective pattern habituation could not be accounted for by this model, since patterns cannot be differentiated at the thalamic level (Sharpless and Jasper, 1956). Another objection is that the model cannot account for the effect of cortical injury in bringing about failure of habituation. On the other hand it is plausible that the thalamo – cortical inhibitory system may be mobilized in the later stages of habituation where after prolonged monotonous stimulation the subject becomes sleepy and shows generalized lowered responsiveness to all stimuli.

NEURAL MODELS FOR HABITUATION: TWO-STAGE MODELS: SOKOLOV

We now turn to what may be termed "two-stage models" of habituation. These are models which embody one stage in which there is an analysing mechanism to determine whether the stimulus

D

necessitates an orientation reaction (i.e. is novel, significant, etc.); and then a second stage in which excitatory or inhibitory mechanisms are set in train to evoke or suppress the orientation reaction. The most fully worked out of these models is that of Sokolov (1960, 1963a), but this position has also been taken by Jouvet (1961) and Moruzzi (1960).

SOKOLOV

The model for the orientation reaction put forward by Sokolov (1960) has been described in Chapter 2 and shown in diagrammatic form in Fig. 1. This model handles both the elicitation of the orientation reaction and the blocking of it with habituated stimuli. To restate the theory briefly: incoming stimuli are conveyed to the cerebral cortex for analysis. The cortex contains many "nervous models", i.e. traces of past stimulation. If the stimulus is a novel one it naturally will not match a nervous model; excitatory impulses are then sent to the reticular formation and the orientation reaction is set in train.

The mechanism proposed for blocking is that the cortex, on matching the incoming stimulation with a nervous model, sends down impulses to the afferent collaterals to block the non-specific input which normally helps to elicit an orientation reaction. This blocking may take place by hyperpolarization of the synaptic connections but this is a matter for speculation. Stimulation is able to pass up to the cortex and down again in time to block the non-specific input through the collaterals because of the slower conduction rates in the collaterals, which is itself a result of the short axons and large number of synapses. In this manner, in Sokolov's terminology, habituated stimuli elicit an inhibitory conditioned reflex.

This notion of a nervous model gives rise to certain difficulties. One is that significant stimuli continue to elicit orientation reactions after they have ceased to be novel and therefore match a nervous model; Sokolov has been obliged to make an additional assumption to account for this (see Chapter 5). Another difficulty arises from what may be termed "sequential habituation", i.e. habituation to sequences of events. The usual situation in which a constant stimulus is presented many times to the subject does not occur so frequently in everyday life as situations in which a sequence of different stimuli occur in regular and predictable order. In these situations we appear to habituate the order of the sequence and the event which gives rise to an orientation reaction is not so much the stimulus itself as the unexpectedness of the stimulus in the sequence in which it occurs. For example, if we are driving a car and see another car approaching on the other side of the road, we give an orientation reaction when the other car swerves in an unexpected direction. Here it would seem to be not so much the actual stimulus of the car which elicits the orientation reaction as the unexpectedness of its swerve in the sequence we have been following. An ingenious method of isolating the physical properties of the stimulus from its position in a sequence has been devised by Unger (1964). In this experiment subjects were presented with numbers in sequence (1, 2, 3, 4, etc.) beginning with 1, at intervals of 5–25 seconds. Orientation reactions were measured by finger vasoconstriction. Most subjects reacted to the stimuli and then habituated to a criterion of three successive failures to respond within a range of 9–36 trials. However, after habituation a number presented out of sequence again elicited an orientation reaction, e.g. with 14, 15, 16, *15*, the last 15 elicits an orientation reaction. This shows that it is not the physical properties of the stimulus as such, but the improbability of its occurrence, that elicits the orientation reaction. Sokolov (1960, p. 206) has also recognized this distinction and suggested an information theory approach to the problem, orientation reactions occurring when the probability of the stimulus is low. This would appear to appreciate Unger's results, even though explaining them may be another matter.

In his interpretation of his findings, Unger argues that the Sokolov "nervous model" must have additional properties to enable it to habituate expected stimuli in advance. It must "be capable of successively and appropriately changing from trial to trial, of virtually reconstituting itself after each succeeding stimulus, to reflect a repeated pre-experimental experience of sequential order, of what follows what, in the stimulus world" (Unger, 1964, p. 17).

It has been argued above that the evidence is against one-stage theories of habituation which assume a fatigue-like inhibitory process in the neurones concerned with analysis of stimuli. Consequently, it would seem that Sokolov and others are correct in assuming a stage of stimulus analysis followed by a second stage of excitation or inhibition of the orientation reaction. These two mechanisms are independent and should be discussed separately. First then Sokolov puts the principal stimulus analysing mechanism in the cerebral cortex (he concedes that there may also be simpler nervous models for analysis in other parts of the nervous system). We must now examine the evidence for this assumption.

The most important evidence is probably the subtlety of the discriminations which the nervous system is able to make between familiar and novel stimuli. Some of these subtle discriminations have been mentioned above, such as the differentiation between stimuli differing only in duration. Another striking discrimination occurs in "semantic habituation". Here it is possible to habituate a subject to a whole group of words of similar meaning, and when a word of different meaning is presented the subject once again gives an orientation reaction. Similar fine discriminations occur in selective habituation to patterns and sequences of stimuli, for example after habituation to simultaneous visual, auditory and tactile stimuli, human beings orientate to one of the stimuli presented by itself. Only animals with a well-developed cortex are capable of these discriminations and the discriminations are lost after cortical damage (Voronin, 1962; Sharpless and Jasper, 1956). This would appear to be powerful evidence for placing the analysing mechanism in the cortex.

THE NEUROPHYSIOLOGY OF THE NERVOUS MODEL

At this stage the reader may well be wondering whether the nervous model, with its remarkable powers of distinguishing novel from familiar stimuli, is not being endowed somewhat loosely with *deus ex machina* properties to explain all the features of the orientation reaction. The theory would gain in plausibility if some direct neurophysiological evidence could be enlisted in support of the existence of the nervous model. Sokolov (1963b) has recognized the desirability of evidence of this kind and gone some way to provide it. First, he assumes that the nervous model consists of three different types of neurons:

1. Afferent neurons: these always respond to a stimulus, even with repeated presentation.

2. Extrapolatory neurons: these only begin to respond to a stimulus after repeated stimulation. With repetition of a stimulus the following sequence takes place:

a. A record of the sequence of stimuli is fixed in the neurons by molecular mechanisms.

b. The neurons generate a sequence of nervous impulses which anticipates the future impulse. There is a similarity between this notion and Anokhin's "acceptor of action" principle. This process can be regarded as a simple form of conditioning and is an attempt to deal with the appearance of an orientation reaction to an unexpected stimulus, i.e. a stimulus which is unusual in the sequence which is occurring.

3. Comparator neurons: these compare signals coming from afferent and extrapolatory neurons. If the stimulus is a novel one the two signals do not match and the comparator neurons then initiate the orientation reaction. It is the activation of these neurons which give rise to local EEG desynchronization. With repetition of a stimulus the signals from the afferent and extrapolatory neurons come to match, the comparator neurons are not activated and local EEG desynchronization ceases.

There is some neurophysiological evidence for the existence of these three types of neurons. *Afferent neurons:* Jung (1961) has found that some neurons in the visual cortex never habituate to flashes of light. The existence of *extrapolatory neurons* is supported by the work of Lettvin, Maturana, Pitts and McCulloch (1961), who report what they call "sameness neurons" in the tectum of the frog. These neurons begin to respond only after the stimulus has been presented several times. The *comparator neurons* may be the "attention units" found by Hubel, Henson, Rupert and Galambos (1959) in the auditory cortex of the cat; these neurons are only activated by novel stimuli. Similar neurons have been found in the frog tectum by Lettvin *et al.* (1961). These studies go some way to increasing confidence in the theory of the nervous model.

INHIBITORY ROLE OF THE CORTEX IN HABITUATION

If the cortex analyses the stimulus as a familiar one it initiates an inhibitory blocking action on the orientation reaction. It is evident that at this point Sokolov's model can be broken down into a general and a specific hypothesis. Generally, it is proposed that the cortex, on matching the incoming stimulus with an existing nervous model, sends down inhibitory impulses which prevent the orientation reaction from occurring. It is then proposed, specifically, that the blocking action takes place in the afferent collaterals.

Considering first the more general hypothesis that in habituation the cortex initiates inhibitory influences which block the orientation reaction, a number of pieces of supporting evidence can be cited.

1. Decortication abolishes or severely impairs habituation and partial decortication retards habituation according to its extent. Here the inhibitory function of the cortex has been impaired or destroyed. The quicker habituation of phylogenetically higher animals with more cortex can be explained along similar lines.

2. Time relations in habituation of components of the orientation reaction. The autonomic components are habituated first, followed later by the EEG hypersynchronization in the analyser of the sense organ being stimulated. The explanation for this is that the autonomic components are blocked by active inhibitory impulses from the cortex. With further repetition of the stimulus the cortex itself becomes inhibited, following the lines of Pavlov's original theory. As the cortex becomes inhibited slow waves characteristic of low arousal begin to appear. This inhibition weakens the control exercised by the cortex on the reticular formation. Hence with further stimulation and inhibition in the cortex the reticular formation is released from cortical control and the orientation reaction is restored. At this stage any situation that can reactivate the cortex (such as giving the subject a task) reactivates the habituation and blocks the orientation reaction. Presumably therefore the cortex is playing an active role in habituation.

3. Eventually the subject goes to sleep. This is explained by incorporating Pavlov's original theory of the spread of inhibition first in the cortex and then downwards. Sharpless and Jasper (1956) have challenged this theory on the basis of their experiment carried out to test it. In this experiment they habituated a cat to a 500 cps tone and then stimulated the animal with an air puff. The cat gave a normal reaction to the air puff, whereas from Pavlov's theory we should have expected the response to be reduced owing to the spread of inhibition. However, it seems possible that the cat was not habituated long enough for the inhibitory processes to spread, since in experiments where there is considerably prolonged habituation, weaker responses to other stimuli do in fact occur. A typical experiment is the following one of Sokolov (1963a, p. 124), in which the subject was habituated to a tactile stimulus on a particular part

of the wrist and the PGR recorded. After some trials, stimulation of adjacent areas of the wrist failed to evoke any response, but stimulation of other skin areas continued to produce responses, although these were weaker than normal. Further, the reduction in size of reaction follows the known cortical representation of skin areas in the cortical receptor area, regions closer to the originally habituated region showing the greatest reduction in reactivity. This gives some support to Pavlov's theory of the irradiation of inhibition. On the other hand, Sokolov himself agrees that this irradiation is fairly limited and does not spread beyond the cortical analyser subjected to stimulation. Consequently Sharpless and Jasper's objection must be allowed to stand and the development of sleep after prolonged habituation remains a puzzle for Sokolov's theory.

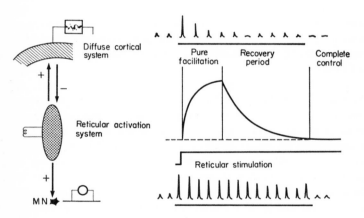

Fig. 12. Records and graph at upper right show facilitation of successive spinal reflex discharge by midbrain reticular stimulation. As cortical excitability is concomitantly elevated, a negative cortico–reticular feedback reduces reticular excitability, marked by decline or loss of reflex facilitation (see schema at left). After decortication (lower record at right), reticulo–spinal facilitation is no longer reduced. (From Hugelin and Bonvallet, 1957.)

4. Confirmatory evidence for the inhibitory role of the cortex comes from the work of Dell, Bonvallet and Hugelin (1961). In these experiments successive reticular activations of the masseteric reflex were observed in preparations with intact cortex and following

decortication. In normal animals reticular stimulation produces only a short phase of facilitation (200–300 msec), followed by a phase in which the masseteric reflex rapidly returns to its original level or is even inhibited (see Fig. 12). After decortication, reticular facilitation of the reflex persists throughout the period of stimulation. The results imply the existence of a negative feedback reticulo – cortico – reticular loop, whereby reticular activation immediately sets in train inhibitory impulses from the cortex. Further evidence supporting this theory comes from measures decreasing cortical tone (e.g. small doses of chloralose, hypocapnia by hyperventilation), which at the same time produce a progressive augmentation of the masseteric reflex by impairing the cortical inhibitory function. These authors conclude that for arousal to take place the stimulus must in some way disrupt the reticulo – cortico – reticular loop.

5. The fact that habituated stimuli continue to elicit evoked potentials in the cortex (e.g. Sharpless and Jasper, 1956) also supports Sokolov's theory, since it indicates that habituated stimuli are reaching the cortex for analysis, even if an orientation reaction does not occur.

These facts taken together must be regarded as fairly strong evidence for the view that the cortex is active in initiating downward inhibitory impulses on the reception of familiar stimuli. There remains now the question of the exact site of blocking. Sokolov assumes that this takes place in the afferent collaterals. To account for the habituation of the generalized orientation reaction before the localized orientation reaction, he assumes that the cortex blocks the non-specific input into the brain stem reticular formation first and into the thalamic reticular formation later. In support of this possibility Sokolov cites the evidence of Benoit (1958), who stimulated the reticular formation electrically and observed no habituation of arousal. The experiments of Olds (1957) on self-stimulation of the arousal system in rats exemplifies the same point, since self-stimulation is not subject to habituation. However, these experiments do not really support Sokolov's theory. All they show is that when the cortex is by-passed, stimuli are not subject to habituation. They give no direct indication of where the cortex exercises its blockade in the normal animal. Consequently it does not appear that there is any strong positive evidence to support Sokolov's hypothesis that the cortex exerts its inhibitory blockade at the collaterals. On the other hand, it may well be conceded that it is difficult to suggest alternative mechanisms for selective habituation in the initial stages of the process when the animal remains fully awake and responsive to all other stimuli. The alertness of the subject argues against any inhibitory dampening of the reticular formation itself, so that it is certainly plausible to assume that the stimuli are blocked before they can activate the reticular formation, in the manner Sokolov suggests.

There is a difficulty with Sokolov's theory, however, when we consider the onset of drowsiness and sleep with repeated stimulation. It seems probable that to handle this we need to assume a further process involving the inhibition of the reticular formation itself. Theories embodying this assumption have been put forward by Moruzzi, Grastyan and Jouvet.

MORUZZI

The existence of an inhibitory centre in the pons which mediates the inhibitory effect of the cortex on the reticular arousal system has been extensively argued by Moruzzi (1960). This theory makes the following assumptions.

1. The existence of separate activating and inhibitory systems in the brain stem; the inhibitory system is placed at the midpontine level and the activating system just above it at the rostropontine level.

2. Repetitive stimulation builds up the inhibitory system, probably by input from the collaterals of the sensory tracts and also from the cortex.

3. As the inhibitory system becomes activated it dampens the activating system, thereby reducing and eventually eliminating the orientation reaction and finally inducing sleep.

The evidence for the existence of such a midpontine inhibitory system is based on a number of experiments. In these experiments it was found that transection of the brain stem at the upper level of the pons ("the pretrigeminal rostropontine preparation") puts the cat into a state of sleep. But a cut a few millimetres below (midpontine pretrigeminal preparation: mpp) puts the cat into an opposite state of extreme alertness with low voltage fast activity in the EEG. The amount of sleep of these animals is greatly reduced and they cannot habituate repetitive stimuli. The anatomical sites of the transections and EEG records are shown in Fig. 13. These two transections are marked A and B in the diagram. The higher

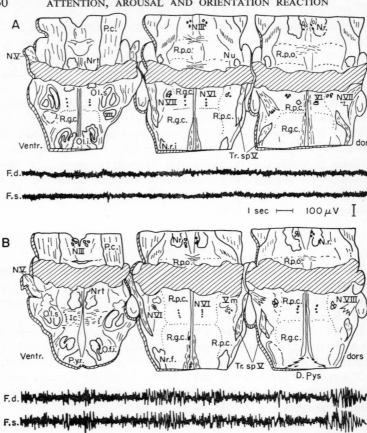

FIG. 13. EEG patterns following midpontine and rostropontine transections. Drawings of horizontal drawings of the cat's brain stem. Cross-hatched areas indicate the level and extent of brain stem lesion in the midpontine (A) and rostropontine (B) pretrigeminal preparations. EEG patterns typical for each preparation, as recorded from right (F.d.) and left (F.s.) frontal areas, are reproduced below each set of drawings. Both types of transection result in the complete interruption of ascending trigeminal influences. Anatomical abbreviations: D.Pyr.: decussatio pyramidum. N.l.l.: nucleus lemnisci lateralis. N.r.: nucleus ruber. N.r.l.: nucleus reticularis lateralis. N.r.t.: nucleus reticularis tegmenti pontis. N. III, V, VI, VII, VIII: root fibres of cranial nerves. Ol.i.: nucleus olivaris inferior. Ol.s.: nucleus olivaris superior. P.c.: pes pedunculi cerebri. Pyr.: pyramis. R.gc.: nucleus reticularis gigantocellularis of Meessen and Olszewski. R.p.c.: nucleus reticularis pontis caudalis of Meessen and Olszewski. R.p.o.: nucleus reticularis pontis oralis of Meessen and Olszewski. Tr.: corpus trapezoideum. Tr.sp.V.: tractus spinalis nervi trigemini. Vm, VI, VII: motor nuclei of cranial nerves. (From Moruzzi, 1960.)

level transection is at point A, severing the connections between the activating system and the cortex and thus producing sleep. The lower level cut is at point B, severing the inhibitory impulses from the inhibitory system to the activating system; as a consequence these animals have long periods of activation, sleep little and cannot habituate.

Further evidence for the existence of an inhibitory system in the pons is derived from experiments in which the blood circulation of the lower brain stem was isolated and injected with barbiturates. The resulting depression of nervous activity in the mid pons area produced EEG arousal in the cortex. Presumably therefore the inhibitory system was temporally blocked by barbiturate injection, releasing the activating system and increasing arousal.

Additional evidence for the existence of an inhibitory system in the brain stem is derived from a number of studies in which the brain stem has been stimulated through implanted electrodes. The stimulation has elicited behavioural and EEG sleep patterns (Caspers and Winkel, 1954; Caspers, 1955; Procter, Knighton and Churchill, 1957; Ingvar and Söderberg, 1958; Favale et al., 1959). Finally, the afferent impulses from the baroceptors of the carotid sinus terminate in this area, in the nucleus of the solitary tract. It is known that stimulation of the carotoid sinus produces sleep (Koch, 1932) and EEG synchronization (Bonvallet, Dell and Hiebel, 1954).

Further work by Moruzzi and his associates has been concerned with systematic electrical stimulation of different areas in the pons to isolate the nuclei involved in the inhibitory system. Synchronizing effects were only obtained from the tractus solitarius, the nucleus of the solitary tract, and the nucleus reticularis ventralis (Magnes, Moruzzi and Pompeiano, 1961).

There is no doubt that the existence of Moruzzi's midpontine inhibitory system is well supported by a number of strands of evidence. We may now turn to its relevance, if any, to habituation. Moruzzi assumes that repetitive stimuli increase the activity of the midpontine inhibitory system and this dampens arousal, blocking the orientation reaction and also the tonic activating impulses to the cortex and thus causing sleep. Moruzzi does not commit himself to the site of the inhibitory action of the midpontine inhibitory system: it may act direct on the upper pontine activation system but it may by-pass this system and block the activation effect higher up, possibly by activating the thalamic inhibitory system. There is at present no direct evidence that the midpontine inhibitory system is involved in habituation in the way Moruzzi suggests. Direct confirmation of the theory would necessitate a demonstration that the electrical activity of this system increases *pari passu* with habituation and this demonstration is crucial to the theory. Nevertheless, there is indirect evidence in favour of the Moruzzi hypothesis, as follows.

Dell, Bonvallet and Hugelin (1961) have compared rates of habituation of EEG desynchronization to stimulation of the mesencephalic reticular formation in normal and mpp cats. With normal cats the EEG desynchronization disappears after about

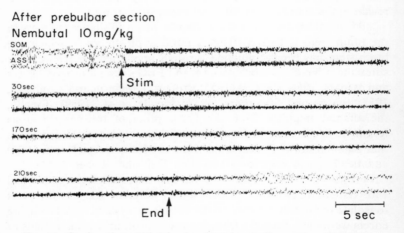

FIG. 14. Cord section at Th 2 level and total prebulbar section. Nembutal 10 mg/kg. Cortical effect of a very long-lasting stimulation of the reticular mesencephalic formation. The cortical activation remains intense during the 4 min of continuous stimulation. (Records between the 40th and the 170th sec are not reproduced here.) (From Dell, Bonvallet and Hugelin, 1961.)

20 sec of stimulation, but with mpp cats no habituation can be obtained up to as long as $4\frac{1}{2}$ min. These differences are illustrated in Fig. 14. The same failure of habituation can be obtained with injection of Novocaine (procaine hydrochloride) into the ventromedial part of the bulb. These experiments suggest that the midpontine inhibitory system plays an essential role in habituation which has been eliminated by section of its ascending pathways. Further

confirmation of this theory is obtained from an experiment in which the voltage of the mesencephalic reticular stimulation is progressively increased from 0 to 2 V in one minute; in encéphale isolé cats only a slight arousal effect is obtained, presumably because habituation counteracts the increasing stimulation. But after prebulbar section, the stimulation produces marked arousal which becomes more intense as the voltage increases.

The importance of the midpontine inhibitory system in habituation has been confirmed by Palestrini and Lifschitz (1961). These authors performed the same midpontine section on cats; they found that these midpontine cats were capable of paying attention to a moving object, but that they do not habituate. In this experiment the cortical evoked potentials were recorded to flashes presented at the rate of 1/sec. Compared with normal cats the midpontine pretrigeminal preparation cats showed larger evoked potentials, a considerable slowing of habituation of primary evoked potentials in the striate cortex (normally habituated after 4200 flashes, not extinguished in mpp cats after 9185 flashes), and failure of habituation of secondary evoked potentials, i.e. those recorded from the gyrus lateralis anterior and suprasylvian gyrus (normals habituate after 20–30 stimuli, mpps still respond after 2200 stimuli). The authors infer from these results that the habituation of cortical evoked potentials is a function of caudal reticular mechanisms. Rostropontine preparations show the same failure of habituation. It should be noted, however, that habituation of cortical evoked potentials is not the same thing as habituation of the orientation reaction, and Affanni, Marchiafava and Zernicki (1962) found that mpp cats habituated orientation reactions to flashes of light quite normally. This is undoubtedly an embarrassment to any theory allotting the pontine inhibitory system a role in habituation.

Thus far the Moruzzi model accounts quite well for the appearance of sleep after prolonged habituation. The monotonous stimulation activates the midpontine inhibitory system, either via the collaterals of the main sensory pathways or via the cortex; the midpontine inhibitory system then blocks the activating system and induces sleep. This leaves unexplained selective habituation of patterns. To account for this Moruzzi assumes (like Sokolov) that the cortex must initially analyse the stimuli. In the case of habituated stimuli, the cortex sends down impulses to the midpontine inhibitory system; this assumption is made to account for the extremely *rapid* onset of sleep that has often been observed after a few presentations of habituated stimuli. On the other hand, novel and significant stimuli continue to elicit the orientation reaction. Here it is assumed that the cortex sends excitatory impulses down to the activating system. Thus the cortex plays an essential part in the activation of the orientation reaction and counteracts the inhibiting impulses from the midpontine inhibitory system.

Moruzzi's theory will be recognized as being similar to that of Sokolov in general structure in so far as it accords the cortex a principal role in stimulus analysis and posits subsequent mechanisms for inhibition or evocation of the reaction. The theories differ in their assumptions of the precise mechanisms of inhibitory action.

GRASTYAN

Another structure which is probably important in the inhibitory mechanisms linking the cortex and the reticular arousal system is the hippocampus. The experiments of Grastyan (1959) have been concerned with recording the electrical activity of the hippo-campus during the presentation of various kinds of stimuli; the results show that all stimuli elicit desynchronization of hippocampal rhythms unless they evoke an orientation reaction. These desyn-chronized hippocampal rhythms result both from completely novel stimuli such as elicit the startle reaction, and from habituated stimuli, whether these have no effect at all or whether they elicit some stable conditioned reaction. But if the stimulus elicits the orientation reaction, the hippocampus gives slow 4–7 cps theta rhythms. The most dramatic demonstration of Grastyan's results is shown in Fig. 15, which shows a simultaneous moving picture of the cat's behaviour and recordings from the hippocampus. Here one second after the presentation of the conditioned stimulus (frame 2), the cat orientates towards the source of the stimulus (frame 4) and at exactly the same time the theta waves appear in the hippocampus. By frame 9 the cat has reached the food and the theta waves from the hippocampus are disappearing. The orientation reaction, together with hippocampal slow waves, occurs to stimuli whose meaning is uncertain such as at the beginning of conditioning when discrimination is introduced after the initial conditioning has become stable, and when the experimenter calls "puss". In this last instance the animal has presumably learned that "puss" heralds some important unconditioned stimulus but is uncertain in the particular stituation about what this is. Very similar facts have been reported by Morrell (1961).

Grastyan's interpretation of these results is that the hippocampus normally exerts a tonic inhibitory effect on the reticular arousal system. With habituated stimuli (such as stable conditioned stimuli as well as totally habituated stimuli), the desynchronization of the

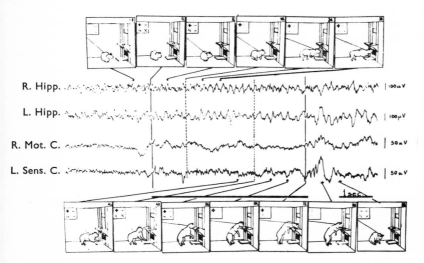

FIG. 15. Demonstration of the simultaneous appearance of the rhythmic slow response and the orientation reaction. Recordings of the motor reaction (moving picture) and the electrical activity are obtained synchronously. Every 8th frame of the moving picture was projected and copied graphically. The moving pictures were taken at a rate of 16 frames/sec. The solid vertical lines indicate the duration of the conditioning stimulus and the dotted vertical lines that of the orientation reaction. The conditioning sound stimulus is also shown by the box flashing the symbol +. The source of the conditioning sound stimulus (loud speaker) is indicated by a black box under the feeding device. As can be seen, the rhythmic slow activity and the orientation reaction coincide. (From Grastyan, 1959.)

hippocampus represents an increase in its inhibitory effects on the reticular formation. It is only when novel and significant stimuli are presented that the hippocampus shows the slow theta activity, representing a decrease of its tonic inhibitory function and a release of the reticular arousal system.

Evidence in favour of the inhibitory function of the hippocampus is available from a number of sources.

1. Microelectrode studies by Purpura (1959, pp. 173–185) give direct support to Grastyan's theory by showing that when theta activity is recorded from the hippocampus it is at the same time giving little efferent output.

2. Stimulation of the hippocampus with implanted electrodes produces desynchronization in the contralateral hippocampus, and inhibits orientation reactions, conditioned reactions and any behaviour in progress (Grastyan, 1959).

3. Presentation of a negative stimulus increases activity in the hippocampus accompanying its inhibitory effect on behaviour (John and Killam, 1960).

4. There is evidence that barbiturates dampen the hippocampus quickly, lessening its tonic inhibitory influence and enhancing reticular evoked potentials for a brief period (Livingstone, 1960).

5. Stimulation of the hippocampus reduces the activating effect of stimulation of the reticular formation for a period of two seconds (Adey et al., 1957).

6. Stimulation of the hippocampus in animals throughout the night has no tendency to awaken them (Olds, 1959).

From this evidence Grastyan's interpretation of the inhibitory role of the hippocampus seems well supported. How is it, he asks (1959), that the hippocampal inhibitory influence is lifted when the orientation reaction is elicited? He does not answer this question but as we have seen the most plausible assumption is that this decision is made in the cortex.

JOUVET

The habituation model proposed by Jouvet (1961) assumes the existence of an inhibitory system in the neocortex. The theory is illustrated in Fig. 16.

The neocortical inhibitory system is activated by repetitive stimuli during habituation. When activated, it sends inhibitory impulses down to the reticular activating system, first blocking the orientation reaction and later inducing sleep. This assumption rests upon the following evidence.

1. Lesions in the neocortex impair habituation; the smaller the amount of cortex left intact, the greater the impairment of habituation; with total removal of the neocortex, habituation is very substantially delayed and Jouvet reports the presence of the orientation reaction after as many as 800 trials.

2. Similarly, repetition of stimuli does not induce sleep in neodecorticated cats.

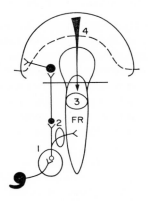

FIG. 16. Jouvet's model for habituation. FR: reticular formation. 1: specific sensory pathways. 2: non-specific pathways. 3: inhibition in reticular formation. 4: inhibitory influences from cerebral cortex. (From Jouvet, 1961.)

3. During habituation there is a marked enhancement of the secondary negative and positive phase of the cortical evoked potentials and a similar enhancement of the secondary wave at the reticular level. It is assumed that these late components of the cortical evoked response are the electrical manifestation of the activation of the neocortical inhibitory system. With further stimulation, spindle bursts and slow waves appear at the cortex and later in the reticular formation and at the same time sleep is induced.

4. Stimulation of certain cortical areas inhibits the potentials normally evoked in the reticular formation by auditory stimuli (Jouvet, Benoit and Courjon, 1956). Similarly, Baumgarten, Mollica and Moruzzi (1954) showed that stimulation of the motor cortex either with strychnine, or electrically, inhibits the spontaneous discharge of reticular units.

E

Jouvet assumes that the neocortical inhibitory system is responsible first for habituation of the orientation reaction and later, with prolonged stimulation, for the first stage of sleep. He assumes also the existence of a caudal inhibitory system in the pons, which is responsible for a second stage of sleep. This system, however, is not activated by repetition of stimuli.

HERNÁNDEZ-PEÓN: AFFERENT NEURONAL HABITUATION

In view of the variety of arguments for postulating a stimulus analysing mechanism in the cortex and subsequent mechanisms for activation or inhibition of the orientation reaction, the work of Hernández-Peón (1960) showing the existence of habituation in the peripheral sensory nuclei may appear discordant. The effect, termed by Hernández-Peón "afferent neuronal habituation", has been demonstrated by recording evoked potentials from electrodes implanted in the peripheral relay nuclei; with repeated stimulation the evoked potentials decrease in size and eventually disappear.

It is important to distinguish this "afferent neuronal habituation" from habituation of the orientation reaction. Hernández-Peón, Jouvet and Scherrer (1957) have observed that habituation of evoked potentials occurs later than habituation of the orientation reaction. This distinction has been confirmed by Gershuni et al. (1960), who showed in cats and hens that after the orientation reaction is totally extinguished to auditory stimuli presented at a rate of 0·4–1·0/sec for several minutes, there was no evidence of habituation of evoked potentials from any part of the auditory pathways. It was only after prolonged stimulation (for some hours) in cats that the gradual fall in evoked potentials appeared in the cortex and the cochlear nucleus. Thus it is likely, as Hernández-Peón (1960) suggests, that different mechanisms are involved in habituation of the orientation reaction and in afferent neuronal habituation.

There has been some dispute about the existence of "afferent neuronal habituation", since not all investigators have been able to obtain the diminution of evoked potentials. On the positive side, one of the earliest findings was that of Artemiev (1951), who reported the disappearance of evoked potentials in the auditory cortex with repeated auditory stimulation. In the peripheral relay nuclei afferent neuronal habituation was first reported by Hernández-Peón and Scherrer (1955) in the cochlear nucleus. Subsequently Hernández-

Peón and his collaborators have found habituation along the specific pathways of vision, smell and touch, the habituation effects being found as low down the specific pathways as the retina, the olfactory bulb and the spinal fifth sensory nucleus (Hernández-Peón, 1960). Habituation of the evoked potentials begins first in the cortex and later in the peripheral relay stations.

Not all investigators have been able to find afferent neuronal habituation. The weight of the evidence suggests that it is only obtained in awake animals, since Sharpless and Jasper (1956) and Jouvet (1961) were unable to find any evidence of it in their sleeping cats. On the other hand, several workers have confirmed the existence of afferent neuronal habituation in awake animals (Galambos, Sheatz and Vernier, 1956; Lifschitz, 1958; Jasper, 1957).

Another variable determining the extent or existence of afferent neuronal habituation may be the time intervals between the stimuli. Sharpless and Jasper (1956) maintain that habituation is only found in the sensory tracts when the stimulation is continuous or the intervals between stimulation are very short. The intervals used by Hernández-Peón have often been short (two per second) but he has also found habituation with interstimuli intervals of the order of 1–3 sec (Hernández-Peón and Scherrer, 1955) and 8–10 sec and even longer (Hernández-Peón and Brust-Carmona, 1961).

Recovery from afferent neuronal habituation can be obtained in a number of ways, viz. (a) after a more or less prolonged period of rest; (b) by application of novel stimuli (dehabituation); (c) by association of the habituated stimulus with a nociceptive stimulus such as an electric shock to the leg; (d) by electrical stimulation in the mesencephalic reticular formation; (e) under barbiturate anaesthesia; and (f) by lesions in the mesencephalic tegmentum. In the last two of these conditions the evoked potentials remain stable and do not habituate.

In considering the mechanisms involved in habituation Hernández-Peón assumes two distinct mechanisms in operation for afferent neuronal habituation and habituation of the orientation reaction. To account for afferent neuronal habituation he postulates the existence of tonic inhibitory impulses, originating from an inhibitory system in the mesencephalic reticular formation and terminating at the synapses in the specific pathways. This system is assumed to intensify the inhibitory discharges during habituation, thereby reducing the evoked potentials in the specific tracts.

There are a number of pieces of evidence bearing on this hypothesis.

1. The strongest support comes from experiments showing that lesions in the mesencephalic reticular formation cause dehabituation and failure of subsequent habituation. Hernández-Peón's results here have been independently confirmed by Moruzzi (1960). (It should be noted that mesencephalic lesions which eliminated acoustic and olfactory habituation did not prevent habituation of vestibular stimulation, but habituation of vestibular stimulation was eliminated by pontine lesions. Thus it is possible that different levels of the brain stem are more related to some and less to other afferent pathways.)

2. The location of the inhibitory system in the mesencephalic reticular formation is further strengthened by elimination of other possibilities. In a series of experiments designed to test these possibilities Hernández-Peón has worked with tactile stimulation on the skin in cats and recorded evoked potentials in the upper thoracic segments of the spinal cord. These evoked potentials habituate with repeated stimulation at the rate of one stimulus every 10 sec. Various parts of the brain were now interfered with. It was found that removal of the neocortex and diencephalon made little difference to habituation rates, if anything decreasing them. These mesencephalic cats who had habituated repeated tactile stimuli were then operated on again and the spinal cord was severed at C2. The tactile evoked potentials were restored and even surpassed the size of the evoked potentials before habituation. This series of experiments (Hernández-Peón and Brust-Carmona, 1961) must be regarded as fairly strong evidence for the location of a tonic inhibitory system in the mesencephalic reticular formation.

3. Barbiturates depress the reticular formation, including the inhibitory centre. Hence the release from habituation of the afferent pathways under barbiturate anaesthesia.

4. There is anatomical evidence of centrifugal fibres terminating at the lower sensory centres (Brodal, 1957), but this is weak evidence in favour of the hypothesis because the origin of these centrifugal fibres is unknown.

5. Electrical stimulation of the brain stem reticular formation blocks afferent volleys at the second order sensory neurones. This mechanism appears to come into operation during selective attention, as has been shown by Hernández-Peón's well-known experiment

in which showing a mouse to a cat blocks the evoked potentials in the cochlear nucleus to irrelevant auditory stimuli (Hernández-Peón, Scherrer and Jouvet, 1956). But this is weak evidence for the habituation hypothesis, because there is no direct evidence that this blocking effect which occurs in selective attention is the same as that occurring in afferent neuronal habituation.

6. Effects of a novel stimulus and electrical stimulation of the mesencephalic reticular formation. Both of these cause dehabituation, attributed by Hernández-Peón to disruption of the inhibitory neurones which maintain habituation. While the evidence does imply the existence of a system of inhibitory neurones which gets disrupted somewhere in the nervous system, it is not strong evidence for its location in the mesencephalic reticular formation.

The conclusion would seem to be that afferent neuronal habituation is a mechanism that comes into play after habituation of the orientation reaction has been accomplished by some other mechanism. Its purpose is presumably to block or attenuate unimportant stimuli peripherally and thus free the higher centres of the brain for more important functions.

CHAPTER 5

CONDITIONED ORIENTATION REACTIONS AND THE ROLE OF THE ORIENTATION REACTION IN CONDITIONING

UP TO this point we have been considering the elicitation and habituation of the orientation reaction by neutral stimuli ("indifferent" or "non-signal" stimuli in Russian translators' prose). We turn now to the effects of transforming a neutral stimulus into a conditioned stimulus. The significance of this transformation is that the stimulus comes to herald or signal the occurrence of some other important stimulus.

METHODS OF CONDITIONING STIMULI

There are various ways of transforming a neutral stimulus into a conditioned stimulus.

1. The neutral stimulus is paired in traditional fashion with an unconditioned stimulus such as pain.

2. The subject can be given instructions to make some motor response when the stimulus occurs; typically in Russian experiments the subject is required to clench his fist or press a bulb at the presentation of the stimulus.

3. Finally, the subject can simply be asked to watch out for the stimulus or pay attention to it.

EFFECTS OF CONDITIONING A STIMULUS

Since the stimulus has now become important to the subject it is advantageous for him to pay full attention to it. This does indeed happen and he makes orientation reactions to it. The effects on the orientation reaction can be particularized as follows:

1. The orientation reaction becomes larger, stronger and quicker than to the same stimulus as a neutral stimulus.

2. If the stimulus has previously been habituated, the orientation reaction to it is restored.

3. The orientation reaction occurs to a wider range of stimuli at

both ends of the intensity scale. First, thresholds are lowered, so that subthreshold stimuli rise above threshold. Secondly, intense stimuli which as neutral stimuli elicit defensive reactions will on being conditioned come to elicit orientation reactions. The biological significance of this change is presumably that it is worth sacrificing the defensive reaction in order to be fully attentive to the forthcoming stimulus.

4. Habituation of the orientation reaction is very considerably slower to conditioned stimuli. For example, Biryukov (1958) reports that young foxes will habituate orientation reactions quite quickly to the sound of mice squeaking, but once they have eaten a mouse the squeaks become conditioned stimuli and the foxes' orientation reactions to them become virtually impossible to habituate.

5. If the stimulus elicits an adaptive reaction, this summates with the orientation reaction.

These effects can now be illustrated in greater detail.

In the first example (Fig. 17) the PGR to tones is measured.

The tones are first presented as neutral stimuli and the subject is given 9 stimulations; it can be seen that the PGR is habituated from the fourth tone onwards. Just after the ninth stimulation he is told to clench his fist whenever he hears the tone. This instruction (giving the stimulus "signal significance" or making it a conditioned stimulus) arouses the subject and produces a very large PGR to stimulus 10. The reaction is now both larger and more resistant to habituation, so that it does not habituate over the next 14 trials. The possibility that the proprioceptive stimuli from the fist clenching are responsible for the revived PGR is eliminated by various controls: the same effects are obtained if the subject is simply asked to attend to the stimuli.

More complicated experiments show that the PGR returns whenever the stimulus changes its significance, i.e. the subject has to make a different response to it. For example, the subject may be required to make a response to one tone but not to another. As the discrimination becomes stabilized the orientation reaction is eliminated. If the stimuli are now "switched", i.e. the positive stimulus made negative and vice versa, the orientation reaction is restored as soon as the negative stimulus is reinforced and the positive stimulus not reinforced. The general level of skin resistance is also lowered, indicating a generalized (tonic) orientation reaction or increase in arousal.

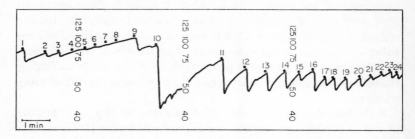

FIG. 17. Intensification of the PGR on the acquisition of signal significance by a stimulus. 1–8: non-signal acoustic stimuli. 9: instructions "close the hand in response to the sound". 10–24: sounds producing movements. Ordinate: resistance (k ohms). (From Sokolov, 1963a.)

The lowering of thresholds for stimuli transformed from neutral stimuli into conditioned stimuli is illustrated in Fig. 18. Here subthreshold light stimuli (of 50 and 25 arbitrary units) are presented to the subject and the EEG, PGR and EMG recorded. In the upper part of the figure there are no reactions. The subject is then asked to react to weak light stimuli, thereby transforming the neutral stimulus into a conditioned stimulus. The subthreshold stimuli now become above threshold and elicit the orientation reaction. The 25 unit stimulus evokes alpha blocking, and the 50 unit stimulus evokes the PGR and EMG reactions as well.

The effects of conditioning painful stimuli (electric shock to the fingers) are illustrated in Figs. 20 and 21. Here the subject is first presented with the stimuli as neutral stimuli; the blood vessel reactions in the hand and in the head are measured (it will be remembered that orientation reactions entail vasoconstriction in the hands and vasodilation in the head, whereas defensive reactions entail vasoconstriction in both the hands and the head). The plethysmograph record of the reaction in the head is recorded in the upper channel and in the hand in the lower channel in the figures. Here, when the pain is initially presented as a neutral stimulus, it can be seen that a stimulus of 3·5 arbitrary units produces no reaction (Fig. 20a). Stimuli of 5 and 7 arbitrary units produce orientation reactions (upward deflection in upper channel: vasodilation in the head; downward deflection of lower channel: vasoconstriction in the hands). Stimuli of 8, 11 and 15 produce defensive reactions (downward deflections in both channels: vasoconstriction in the head and

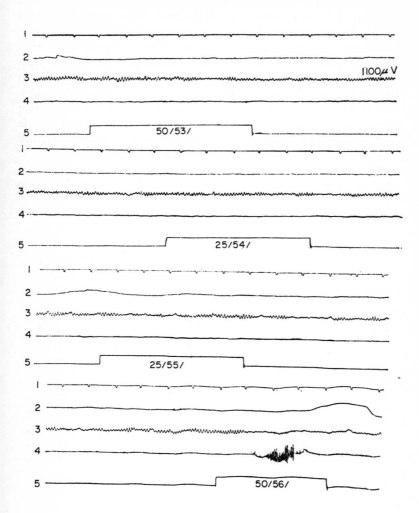

FIG. 18. Enhancement of light sensitivity by instructions to effect response movements to photic stimuli. 1: time. 2: galvanic skin reaction. 3: right occipital EEG. 4: EMG. 5: light stimulus. (From Sokolov, 1963a.)

hands). Thus the orientation reaction is elicited by stimuli in the range of 5–7 units. These stimuli are now made into conditioned stimuli by instructing the subject to pay attention to them. Actually in this experiment the subject is being asked to classify the stimuli as barely perceptible, weak, moderate, slight pain and severe pain.

The effects of this conditioning are shown in Fig. 21. Here it can be seen (b) that stimuli of 3 and 4 now elicit the orientation reaction. The threshold has therefore been lowered. A stimulus of 15 also elicits the orientation reaction, showing that at this intensity the defensive reaction has given way to the orientation reaction. Stimuli of 16, 18 and 20 continue to elicit the defensive reactions.

The widening of the range of stimuli eliciting the orientation reaction after conditioning applies also to auditory stimuli. For some

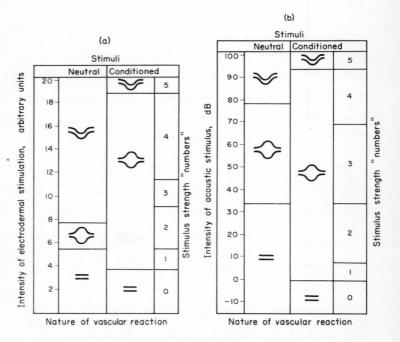

Fig. 19. Relationships between vascular reactions, assessed strengths and level of sensitivity for neutral and conditioned electrodermal and acoustic stimuli. Subject A.S., Electrodermal stimuli. Subject L.A., Acoustic stimuli. (From Sokolov, 1963a.)

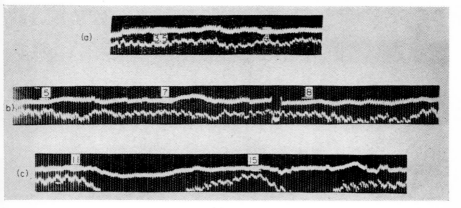

FIG. 20. Unconditioned electrodermal stimulation thresholds for orienting and defensive reflexes. (From Sokolov, 1963a.)

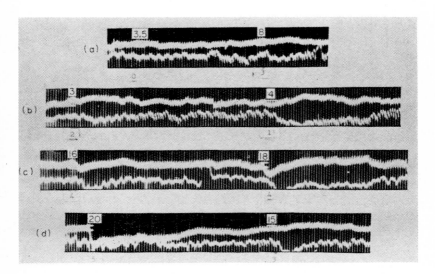

FIG. 21. Thresholds of orienting and defensive reflexes with the strengths of the electrodermal stimuli subjectively classified. (Continuation of Fig. 20.) The numbers below are the strength "numbers" of the stimuli. (From Sokolov, 1963a.)

reason, however, auditory stimuli produce a more striking fall in absolute threshold than rise in the threshold for the defensive reaction, whereas with pain stimuli this tendency is reversed (see Fig. 19).

With repeated application of the conditioned stimulus habituation sets in, leading eventually to the extinction of the orientation reaction. The habituation of conditioned stimuli, however, takes place more slowly. With repetition of the stimulus, therefore, the range of stimuli eliciting the orientation reaction declines so that absolute thresholds rise and the threshold for the defensive reaction falls. When a 70 db tone is applied to a subject, for example, typically it initially evokes vasodilation in the head and is subjectively assessed as mildly painful. With repeated application it evokes vasoconstriction in the head and at the same time is subjectively experienced as being more painful. This effect of habituation is subject to disinhibition, i.e. an extraneous stimulus once more widens the range of stimuli eliciting the orientation reaction and reduces sensitivity to pain.

THE FORMATION OF CONDITIONED RESPONSES

It frequently happens that conditioned stimuli become connected with instrumental responses. For the formation of these conditioned responses, conditioning takes place most readily when the orientation reaction is some way towards being habituated and is less effective both at the beginning when the orientation reactions are strong and when they are totally extinguished. In general terms these effects are probably due to the competition of the orientation reaction with the conditioned response when the orientation reaction is very strong, and the failure of the animal to attend to the conditioned stimulus when the orientation reaction is extinguished. The difficulty of conditioning an animal making strong orientation reactions was noted by Pavlov and attributed to the excitatory state in the cortical centre for the orientation reaction inducing inhibition in the centre for the unconditioned reaction, according to the law of negative induction. The first step in conditioning therefore consists in habituating orientation reactions to both the conditioned and the unconditioned stimuli.

As the conditioned connection becomes formed the orientation reaction becomes weaker until eventually it disappears with complete stabilization of the conditioned reaction. Any change in the conditioning procedures, however, brings back the orientation reaction until the response to the changed situation has once more become stabilized. The chief changes of this kind are extinction, discrimination learning and "switching" (reversal shifts) where the positive stimulus is made negative and vice versa.

We will now give two examples of experiments which show most of these effects, one using aversive conditioning and the other voluntary motor conditioning. In the first example (Sokolov, 1960, pp. 221 ff.) a painful electric shock serves as the unconditioned stimulus, evoking the unconditioned defensive reaction (vasoconstriction in the hands and the head), and a tone is used as the conditioned stimulus. The object of the experiment is to condition the defensive reaction to the tone.

1. Initially, both the electric shock and the tone produce orientation reactions by virtue of their novelty. The orientation reactions must therefore first be habituated. A record of the reactions of one subject is shown in Fig. 22.

2. It takes 17 trials of the tone to habituate the orientation reaction and 47 trials of the electric shock. The electric shock now elicits the defensive reaction (i.e. at this point vasodilation in the head disappears and vasoconstriction takes its place). These effects are shown in Fig. 22A. It is now possible to begin the conditioning.

3. The sound is now paired with the shock. The combination has novelty and therefore the orientation reaction returns (Fig. 22B, left). After 35 trials the tone is conditioned to the shock, i.e. elicits the defensive reaction before the shock occurs (Fig. 22B, right).

4. Discrimination is now attempted. The new stimulus elicits the orientation reaction and is not reinforced by shock. The original tone now also elicits the orientation reaction once again (Fig. 22C, left). After 80 trials the original stimulus reverts to eliciting the defensive reflex (Fig. 22D, right), and after 24 trials the negative stimulus ceases to evoke any reaction (Fig. 22D, left).

5. Two stages in discrimination learning can be distinguished. After a few trials of reinforcing the positive stimulus and not reinforcing the negative stimulus a stage of wide generalization is reached, i.e. many generalized stimuli evoke the defensive reflex. This effect is shown in Fig. 23. In this experiment the subject is only shocked after a 500 cps tone. The generalization effect of the early stage of conditioning is represented by the solid line, which

shows that all tones within the 300–900 cps range elicit the defensive reaction. Beyond this range they elicit the orientation reaction.

6. With further training the subject discriminates the 500 cps tone more finely (Fig. 23, dotted lines). Now only stimuli in the range 490–510 cps elicit the defensive reaction. Frequencies close to this range (450–490 and 510–550 cps) elicit very strong orientation reactions. With more remote frequencies there is no reaction. It is only when the stimuli become so remote as to be novel stimuli (1500 cps and above) that the orientation reaction recurs.

In these experiments it can be seen that the orientation reaction occurs whenever novel or ambiguous stimuli are presented—that is,

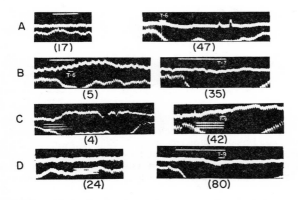

FIG. 22. Relationship between orientation and conditioned reflex. Sound, indicated by long horizontal lines, strength of electric shock indicated in arbitrary units (T–6, T–7, T–9). In (A) to (D): upper traces, vascular reaction in the head; lower traces, in the finger. (A) After the 17th sound and 47th shock, no orienting reflex. Sound alone has no effect (left). Shock alone (T–6, right) produces defensive reflex (vasoconstriction in both head and finger). (B) Combination of sound with shock in elaboration of conditioned reflex at first evokes orientation reaction to both the sound and the as yet unconditioned shock (left, 5th combination). Only after the 35th combination was defensive reflex elaborated (right), i.e. vasoconstriction in the head on sound preceding application of shock. (C) A different sound evokes recovery of orientation reactions to both the new sound and to the previous conditioning stimulus (left). When one sound is reinforced with shock and the other not, the orientation reaction is very marked and persistent. Even after the 42nd presentation and increase of the shock to 9 units, the orientation reaction is still present (right). (D) During elaboration of conditioned reflexes, the differential stimulus becomes ineffective, and the conditioning stimulus begins to evoke the defensive reflex (24th and 80th). (From Sokolov, 1960.)

during the formation of conditioned reactions and discrimination. With stabilization of the reactions, the orientation reaction is habituated. Sokolov assumes the existence of two neuronal models,

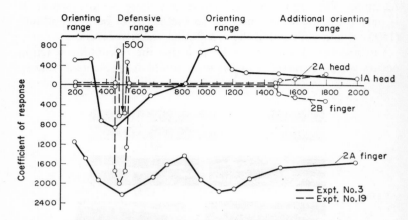

Fig. 23. Relationship between defensive and orientation reactions with increasing numbers of reinforcements by shock (500 cps sound). Abscissa: frequency of sound in cps. Ordinate: magnitude of vascular reaction (area under the curve). Vasodilation, upward. Vasoconstriction, downward. By the third experiment (solid lines), the range of defensive conditioned reflexes is wide (from 300 to 900 cps). The orientation reaction is evoked by all frequencies within this range. In the course of elaboration, the conditioned defensive reflex became very specific to the frequency of 500 cps (broken line, Expt. No. 19). The orientation reaction is evoked most strongly by stimuli which are close in frequency to that of the conditioning defensive stimulus. Additionally, orientation reactions to a range of widely different frequencies develop (right). (From Sokolov, 1960.)

one for the stimulus reinforced with electric shock, the second for stimuli not reinforced. If a stimulus coincides with one or other of these neuronal models it elicits the defensive reflex or no reaction. If it does not coincide by being intermediate between the two or beyond the range of the negative stimulus, the orientation reaction is elicited.

We have seen that in aversive conditioning the orientation reaction occurs first to all stimuli, then disappears as the conditioning becomes stabilized, and reappears when a new stimulus is presented for discrimination. The same sequences take place in voluntary motor conditioning, as the following experiment (Sokolov, 1960, pp. 227 ff.) shows.

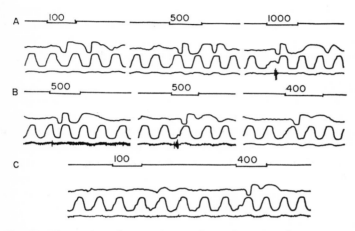

FIG. 24. Elaboration of a negative conditioned motor reflex interpreted by the concept of a "negative model". In (A), (B), and (C), from top to bottom: sound in cps, PGR, respiration, and EMG of flexors. (A) At the start, negative stimulation (100 cps) produced no motor reactions but a strong orientation reaction. Only a stimulus of very different frequency (1000 cps) produced a motor reaction. (B) In the course of repeated comparisons made by the model between negative motor stimulation and stimulation which differed from this, the discriminatory power increased. At first, 500 cps was not effective, but it later evoked a motor reaction. (C) On continuation, the negative model became completely inhibiting, and stimulations which differed from it evoked either the orientation (with very close frequencies) or the motor reactions (with widely different frequencies). Here, 400 cps evoked the orientation reaction without motor reaction. (From Sokolov, 1960.)

In this experiment the subject is instructed not to clench his fist or make any response to a tone of 100 cps, but to clench his fist at all other frequencies of stimulation. The PGR, respiration rates and EMG of the flexors are taken as the indices of the orientation reaction. The subject is then presented with the following discriminations.

1. Stimuli of 100, 400, 500 and 1000 cps are presented in random order. All the stimuli evoke orientation reactions. 100 cps is correctly identified and the subject does not react by clenching his fist to it. However, only the 1000 cps stimulus is correctly discriminated: the subject clenches his fist to this stimulus but not to 400 or 500 cps stimuli. These effects are illustrated in Fig. 24A.

2. With further training, the subject's discrimination becomes finer. He is now perfectly conditioned to 100 cps, producing no motor reaction and no orientation reaction (Fig. 24C). He also discriminates 500 cps (Fig. 24B). But he fails to discriminate 400 cps, which still produces an orientation reaction and no motor reaction (Fig. 24B).

3. When a stimulus is being discriminated, the subject first produces the correct response accompanied by an orientation reaction. Then as the correct response becomes stabilized with further trials, the orientation reaction begins to disappear. This sequence is shown in Fig. 24B, where the subject is learning to discriminate 500 cps; he gives the correct motor reaction and an orientation reaction as well. Later, with stabilized discrimination, the subject produces the correct motor reaction without any orientation reaction.

CONDITIONING HABITUATED STIMULI

How far does the orientation reaction occur in conditioning simply because of the novelty of the stimuli or the combination of stimuli, or how far is it essential in the formation of the conditioned link so that the conditioned association cannot be formed without it? The Russians favour the view that it plays a vital part and urge two chief pieces of evidence in support of this.

1. In newly born animals orientation reactions do not occur in complete form (see Chapter 6) and conditioned instrumental responses are impossible. Conditioned instrumental responses become possible only a day or two after the behavioural investigation component of the orientation reaction has developed (Vinogradova, 1961). It should be noted that this argument, like the succeeding one, applies only to instrumental conditioning and may suggest

that the orientation reaction does play some part in this kind of conditioning. Classical conditioning can of course occur without the awareness of the subject and without orientation reactions (Razran, 1961).

2. In situations where the subject has first been habituated to the stimulus to be conditioned, conditioning occurs in two stages. In the first stage, the orientation reaction to the stimulus is revived; in the second stage, once this has occurred, the stimulus response connection can be formed. Sokolov (1963a, pp. 247–249) infers that this indicates the necessary role of the orientation reaction during conditioning. It is as if the subject has to learn first that the stimulus is significant, and then what reaction has to be made to it. Why is this? Sokolov maintains that the orientation reaction raises the levels of excitation in the cortical centres of the conditioned and unconditioned stimuli and that this facilitates the formation of the link between them.

These facts can be illustrated in the following experiment, in which the subject is conditioned to raise his hand to a habituated tone. The conditioning is carried out by instructing the subject to raise his hand three or four seconds after the presentation of the tone. The instruction acts here as the unconditioned stimulus. If the tone has not been presented to the subject before, it elicits an orientation reaction and the conditioning is established very quickly, in 2–3 trials. However, if the tone is first habituated the conditioning takes much longer and the orientation reaction to it must first be revived. These effects are shown in Fig. 25. The stimulus is first habituated, and the lack of any reaction to the 10th presentation is shown at the beginning of the figure. The unconditioned stimulus "Raise the hand" instruction is now given and elicits an orientation reaction, measured here by alpha blocking, PGR and EMG reactions. The subject shows a little evidence of conditioning on the next (12th) trial, with a small PGR, which becomes stronger with succeeding reinforcements on the 13th and 14th trials. But the motor response, measured by the EMG, does not occur to the tone by the 25th trial and only emerges as a conditioned reaction by the 26th trial. In some experiments of this kind a conditioned reaction has not been formed after 60 or more trials. Subjects report that they are not conscious of paying any attention to the habituated neutral stimulus.

F

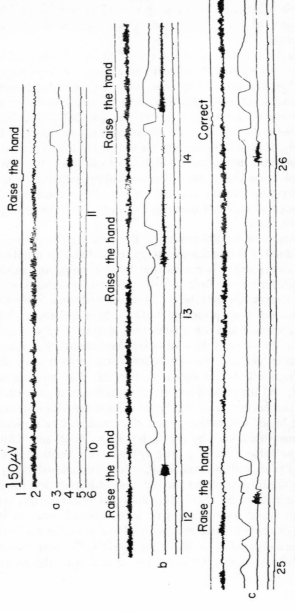

FIG. 25. Reappearance of the orientation reaction before conditioning is established. 1: verbal reinforcement. 2: EEG. 3: galvanic skin reaction. 4: EMG. 5: time. 6: stimulus (sound of 1000 cps, 70 db). (From Sokolov, 1963a.)

RECIPROCAL INHIBITION RELATIONSHIP OF THE ORIENTATION
REACTION AND THE CONDITIONED REFLEX

Where the conditioned reflex has not been completely learned and the stimulus therefore still elicits the orientation reaction, a reciprocal inhibition relationship appears to exist between the orientation reaction and the conditioned reflex, so that the orientation reaction momentarily prevents the conditioned reflex from occurring. The purpose of this momentary inhibition is presumably to give the subject time to evaluate the stimulus before committing himself to a reaction.

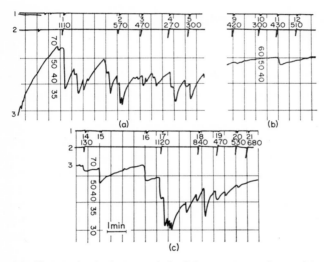

FIG. 26. Changes in the latent period of the motor reaction and in the strength of the orientation reaction on introduction of stimulus differentiation. 1: acoustic stimulus. 2: latent period of motor reaction in sigmas (pressure on a key, whereby the latent period of the motor reaction was measured simultaneously). 3: galvanic skin reaction. Ordinate: resistance (k ohms). (From Sokolov, 1963a.)

The inhibitory effect of the orientation reaction is illustrated in the following experiment. Here the subject is instructed to press a key on hearing a 1000 cps tone. Figure 26a shows the subject's initial reaction: to the first stimulus there is a large orientation reaction (measured here by the PGR) and a slow motor reaction. With repetitions, the orientation reaction gets smaller and the motor conditioned reflex faster. On trials 10–14 new stimuli of 400–200 cps are presented and the subject makes small orientation reactions and fairly quick motor reactions. After trial 14, however, the subject is required to differentiate and is told "There is no need to press the key in response to this sound" (a 200 cps tone). The next applications of 200 cps (trial 15) and 300 cps (trial 16) tones produce no motor reactions and large orientation reactions. On trial 17 the original positive 1000 cps tone is presented again: it now produces a large orientation reaction because the discrimination has not yet been fully learned, and a slow motor reaction. In these experiments it is only after the orientation reaction has subsided that the motor conditioned reflex takes place. Hence the assumption that the purpose of the delay is to allow a brief period for evaluation of the stimulus.

ORIENTATION REACTIONS IN MENTALLY DEFECTIVE CHILDREN

A further piece of evidence indicating the importance of the orientation reaction in the learning process is derived from the inadequacy of the orientation reaction in mentally defective children. It is argued by Luria (1963) that the well-known defects in attention and poor learning of mental defectives are a result of poor orientation reactions. The characteristics of the orientation reactions of mentally defective children are as follows. First, they frequently do not give orientation reactions to low and medium intensity stimuli. They will give orientation reactions to intense stimuli, and these reactions are powerful and difficult to extinguish. These characteristics are attributed to defects of cortical functioning. In the case of low and medium strength stimuli the cortex does not facilitate an orientation reaction; or, if it does produce a reaction it is weak and disappears after one or two trials. Intense stimuli elicit an orientation reaction by direct stimulation of the reticular formation, and the cortex then fails in its habituation function, so that the mentally defective child does not habituate like normal children.

A second peculiarity about orientation reactions in mentally defective children is that they cannot be prolonged by verbal instruction. In normal children, just as in adults, instruction to pay attention to a stimulus greatly extends the number of orientation reactions given to it, but this effect cannot be obtained in mentally defective children.

Luria shows that there is a close correlation between these imperfections in the functioning of the orientation reaction and the learning difficulties of the mentally defective. There are three distinct kinds of impairment. First, the mentally defective child does not pay attention to novel stimuli because he does not produce orientation reactions to them. This leads to a failure of learning because, as Sokolov also shows, orientation reactions are essential for the formation of conditioned reactions. Thus in experiments where a neutral stimulus precedes the instruction "Press the bulb", the normal child produces an orientation reaction to the neutral stimulus and is conditioned to it (i.e. presses the bulb on presentation of the stimulus) after two or three trials. The mentally defective child does not give an orientation reaction and is not conditioned, in this respect resembling a normal subject who has first been habituated to the stimulus.

A second defect in the mentally defective child is that orientation reactions are still given to intense irrelevant stimuli, whereas a normal child absorbed in some task will not give these irrelevant orientation reactions. This is the cause of the distractibility of mentally defective children. The third defect is the failure of verbal conditioning, which makes it impossible to direct the attention of the mentally defective child by verbal instruction. For example, the instruction "Count the stimuli" does not produce continued orientation reactions to the stimuli in the mentally defective child as it does in normal children. This defect naturally leads to great difficulty in learning in the classroom. A mentally defective child can sometimes be taught a reaction for a brief period, but the learning quickly breaks down. For example, it is possible to teach discrimination of two metronome beat rates, so that the child reacts to one and not to the other. After a few trials, however, the mentally defective child ceases to give orientation reactions to the two stimuli, and at the same time the correct reaction breaks down. In the normal child, as with adults, orientation reactions continue to be evoked until the motor reactions have become stabilized and "automatic".

NEUROLOGICAL MECHANISMS FOR THE EFFECTS OF CONDITIONING STIMULI

We have seen that when a habituated stimulus is conditioned it again evokes an orientation reaction; furthermore, this reaction is larger than originally and considerably more resistant to habituation. What are the neurological mechanisms underlying these effects? Sokolov suggests that excitation increases in the motor analyser accompanying the performance of the motor response and that this excitation spreads to the analyser responsible for the perception of the conditioned stimulus. This spread of excitation increases the excitation in the perceptual analyser and hence increases the size of the orientation reaction and its resistance to habituation.

How far is this notion of a flow of excitation in the opposite direction plausible? Sokolov argues that it can be demonstrated in the following experiment of Pavlov: here a dog is conditioned to lift its paw when it is hungry, i.e. the stimulus of salivation evokes the response of paw lifting. Then when the dog's paw is lifted passively, it salivates. To explain this we must assume a two-way connection between the centres for salivation and paw lifting so that the excitation of either leads to excitation of the other.

It does not seem entirely convincing, however, to draw a parallel between the situation in Pavlov's experiment and some of the situations used by Sokolov. In the situation where a neutral stimulus is associated with pain, it may not seem too implausible to suppose that a two-way connection becomes established between the pain analyser and the neutral stimulus analyser, so that the pain analyser raises the excitation of the neutral stimulus analyser and makes it more responsive. Sokolov is proposing that simply instructing the subject to watch out for the stimulus raises the excitation level in the same way. Even if this mechanism is accepted it does not account for the fact that some conditioned stimuli become completely immune from habituation.

IS THE ORIENTATION REACTION A CONDITIONED OR AN UNCONDITIONED REACTION?

It was assumed by Pavlov that the orientation reaction is an unconditioned reflex to novel stimuli and this view has been virtually universally accepted. Recently, however, it has been challenged by Grastyan (1961), who has argued that it is better regarded as a quickly conditioned reaction. This argument is based on the following facts.

1. Unfamiliar stimuli do not evoke the behavioural orientation reaction or the hippocampal slow (theta) waves which Grastyan has

found invariably accompany the orientation reaction. The orientation reaction only appears after several applications of the stimulus. A completely new stimulus elicits the startle response, which takes the form of a quick, phasic movement of the head towards the stimulus but lacks the investigatory character of the true orientation reaction. In making this distinction Grastyan distinguishes between the protective purpose of the startle reaction and the investigatory purpose of the orientation reaction, along the same lines as Russian investigators (see Chapter 1). But although the behavioural distinction between the startle and orientation reactions may be somewhat difficult to make, there is a clear-cut electrophysiological distinction because the orientation reaction is accompanied by hippocampal theta rhythms, whereas the startle reaction is accompanied by hippocampal desynchronization. This is an interesting example of a striking electrophysiological distinction forcing the recognition of a behavioural distinction between the two only slightly different types of behavioural reaction to novel stimuli.

2. A second consideration in support of Grastyan's position is that the orientation reaction can easily be habituated and in this respect resembles conditioned rather than unconditioned reactions.

3. The absence of the orientation reaction in infancy and its emergence several weeks after birth add further strength to Grastyan's position. Although it remains possible that it may emerge by maturation, the fact that the motor equipment for the reaction appears to emerge (taking the form of defensive reactions) well before the orientation reaction itself suggests that the orientation reaction is learned.

CHAPTER 6

THE ORIENTATION REACTION IN ONTOGENETIC AND PHYLOGENETIC DEVELOPMENT

ORIENTATION REACTIONS IN THE NEWLY BORN

The orientation reaction does not appear in the completely developed form in the newly born or for some time after birth, either in human infants or in a variety of mammals including rabbits and dogs (Vinogradova, 1961). However, while some components of the orientation reaction are completely absent, other components are present. The considerable body of Russian research on this topic is reviewed by Vinogradova and the following conclusions emerge.

1. Automatic reactions. These reactions do occur in part in the newly born. For example, Bronstein, Itina, Kamenetskaya and Sytova (1958) obtained respiratory arrest in a 72-hour-old human infant in response to a flash of light, although this reaction extinguished quickly, in 5 trials. Frequently, newly born animals have a different pattern of reaction from that of adults and the PGR is generally not present, and only emerges in kittens and human babies after some weeks and at the same time as the active behavioural investigation component of the orientation reaction. When the PGR is obtained it is smaller in the first year of life in human infants than in older children (Jones, 1930). Vasoreactions are also weaker in newly born infants than in older children and adults. On the other hand, the heart rate reactions of 3–7-year-old children are greater than those of older children (Vinogradova, 1961). In infants of some species the autonomic reactions of the newly born may be opposite in direction from those of adults. For example, in newly born human infants, monkeys and puppies, stimulation produces a slowing of breathing and heart rate, whereas in the adults these are accelerated (after an initial pause in respiration) (Nikitina and Novikova, 1958). According to these investigators the arousal pattern of the newly born resembles that of decorticated

80

animals and occurs in the newly born because the cortex does not at this stage control the orientation reaction. It is only when the cortex is developed that the adult pattern of autonomic reaction emerges. For example, in dogs the cortex is morphologically mature at 6–8 weeks and the adult reaction pattern occurs at 8–12 weeks.

2. Cessation of ongoing activity. This component is also present in the newly born. The only ongoing activity which is likely to be in progress in human infants is sucking and this is checked by auditory stimuli some 2–3 hr after birth (Bronstein *et al.*, 1958). In Bronstein's experiments on human infants, cessation of sucking to auditory stimuli was obtained in 82 per cent of subjects, to visual stimuli in 67 per cent, and to olfactory stimuli in 20 per cent. In comparing human infants with animals, Bronstein considers that human infants are more reactive: for example, reactions to light could only be obtained in 20 per cent of baby rabbits, 21 per cent of baby puppies and 37 per cent of kittens as against 67 per cent of human infants. If the reaction occurs, its extinction is also quicker in animals, generally occurring after one or two presentations of the stimulus. Another phenomenon differentiating human infants from animals is that disinhibition of extinguished reactions is much more common in human babies.

One of the most thorough Western studies of the reaction of newly born infants is that of Bridger and Reiser (1959). The subjects in these experiments were 3-day-old babies. Bridger and Reiser concluded that there were two kinds of reaction. First, a generalized non-specific startle-like response, which can be elicited by an air puff on the abdomen. The change in heart rate produced by the stimulation depends on the level of heart rate before stimulation. If the baby is sleeping or drowsy, the pre-stimulus heart rate is low and the heart rate response is large. When the baby is more aroused, with higher resting level heart rate, the heart rate response is smaller. There comes a point where the reaction to stimulation is a decrease in heart rate. This finding conforms to the "law of initial value", according to which reactivity is inversely related to resting level. Bridger suggests that this may be regarded as an orientating reaction, but it is of course only one component of it.

The second response noted by Bridger and Reiser is a specific local sucking response to air puffs on the mouth. This reaction does not obey the law of initial values, and the higher the resting level of heart rate the more vigorous the reaction.

Bridger has also presented data on habituation of the startle reaction in newly born babies, stimulating with a tone of 20 sec duration with intervals of 10 sec. The startle reaction habituates in two stages; first there is a powerful startle reaction that habituates out in eight to ten responses; there are then lesser responses to many more than 30 repetitions of the stimulus. The response here is behavioural startle as rated by observers. It is a matter of everyday observation that with adults and children, behavioural startle to an auditory tone does not occur after the first trial or two, and it would therefore appear that Bridger's results indicate that habituation is much slower in newly born infants.

In further experiments Bridger has varied the duration of the tone, the intervals between the tones, and the frequency of the tones. His results can be summarized briefly. Habituation is facilitated the shorter the interval between the stimuli and the longer the stimulus; these effects are also found in adults (see Chapter 1). About half of newly born babies in the first 5 days of life can discriminate a tone of 400 cps from one of 1000 cps in that having habituated one they produce a full startle reaction to the other. With prolonged loud stimulation for 40 or 50 sec, infants frequently go to sleep. This could be a useful discovery for parents.

3. Behavioural orientation. It is this component of the orientation reaction, the turning reaction towards the source of stimulation, that is completely lacking in newly born mammals and only emerges a few weeks after birth. Thus it is possible to distinguish between the autonomic components of the orientation reaction which are present immediately after birth, and the motor components responsible for the purposive activity which develops some time after birth. As the motor components develop, the animal comes to make either orientation – investigation approaches to the stimulus, or defensive – withdrawal movements away from it.

The age at which the behavioural components of the orientation reaction emerge has been studied in various animals. For example, Obraztsova, Pomazanskaya, Stel'makh and Troshikhin (1958) investigated this question in puppies and baby rabbits and concluded that three stages of development can be differentiated:

1–25 days: autonomic reactions but no behavioural orientation or defensive reaction. All stimuli tend to evoke feeding reactions, e.g. salivation and sucking.

20–40 days: a reaction of "biological caution" or "passive defensive reaction": the animal tries to shield itself from the stimulation.

45 days onwards: the normal orientation reaction to moderate stimuli or active aggressive - defensive reaction to strong stimuli.

The same three stages of the development of reactions are reported in human infants by Polikanina and Probotova (1958) and Degtyar (1963). In Degtyar's investigation the reactions of 35 newly born infants to visual and auditory stimuli were investigated during the first 80 days of life. Bright lights elicited adaptive reactions (pupil constriction) immediately after birth. Fixation of the gaze on a bright object, which may be taken as a rudimentary component of the orientation reaction, occurred at 5 days in 5 children, at 10 days in half the children, and in all the 35 children at 14 days. Following a moving light appeared in 2 children at 10 days, in half the children by 14 days, and in all the children at 4 weeks. Turning the head towards the source of auditory stimulation emerged somewhat later, in the second month of life in half the children.

The development of orientation reactions in young puppies has been investigated by Nikitina (1954). She distinguishes between immature (i.e. poorly executed) and mature orientation reactions. Puppies will give immature orientation reactions to auditory stimuli at the age of 10–15 days, and to visual stimuli at 15–19 days; this difference reflects the later maturation of the visual analyser, since puppies are not able to see until about 13–14 days after birth. These immature orientation reactions consist of a diminution or cessation of whimpering and in a slight raising of the head, and they have a long latency of from 3–6 sec compared with about 1 sec in the mature animal.

The mature orientation reaction emerges between the 16th and 24th day after birth. Conditioned defensive reactions also become possible at the same time. But although the orientation reaction now occurs in its mature form, it is still difficult to habituate it and the adult speed of habituation does not occur until 35 to 50 days.

CONDITIONED ORIENTATION REACTIONS IN INFANTS

A study designed to make clear the earliest age at which it is possible to condition orientation reactions in human infants has been reported by Kasatkin, Mirzoyants and Khokhitva (1953). The babies lay in cots with an electric light bulb hanging on one side of their heads. From about 6 weeks onwards the babies gave orientation reactions towards the light bulb when it was illuminated, first in the form of eye movements towards the light and later with head movements as well. The authors now attempted to condition these orientation reactions by presenting a tone before the onset of the light (the tone was presented directly behind the baby's head to prevent orientation to the tone). They found some conditioning was possible at about $2\frac{1}{2}$ months, but at this age the conditioning takes a number of trials and is unstable. At the age of around 5–7 months the orientation reaction becomes stably conditioned in two or three trials and is extinguished in about the same number, with some spontaneous recovery on later days.

A study by Rogov (1955) reports developmental differences in conditioning the orientation reactions to a neutral stimulus, using vaso-reactions as an index of the orientation reaction. In an age range of 3–10 years younger children condition more quickly. At 3–5 years the children conditioned in an average of 18 trials, 6–7-year-olds took 40 trials, and 8–10-year-olds 50 trials. These differences are attributed to a decrease in the predominance of excitatory processes in children during this age range. The theory that young children have weak inhibitory and strong excitatory processes is widely accepted in Russia and has been extensively argued by Luria (1961).

HABITUATION IN YOUNG ANIMALS

Studies of habituation rate in ontogenetic development have given rise to some conflicting findings, some investigators claiming that the young habituate quickly and others that they habituate slowly. These contradictions concern the newly born. It would appear that there is first a stage at which the orientation reaction does not occur or is very weak, and at this stage it will extinguish in one or two trials if it does occur (Bronstein, Itina, Kamenetskaya and Sytova, 1958). Subsequently the orientation reaction develops and is at first more resistant to extinction than when the animal becomes adult. Some investigators have found that it is impossible to habituate the reactions of some young animals and they go on reacting until they fall asleep (Vinogradova, 1961). Some detailed results on ontogenetic differences in habituation rates in puppies have been presented by Nikitina (1954). In puppies aged 3–14 days, the orientation reaction to sounds takes some 200 trials to extinguish, whereas puppies aged 40–60 days extinguish in some 15–20 trials.

The long time taken by young animals to habituate is attributed by Russian investigators to the incomplete development of the cortex, which is held to play an important part in the habituation mechanism. In addition to the fairly extensive evidence in support of this hypothesis reviewed in Chapter 4, the ontogenetic data provide additional evidence. This is that the morphological maturity of the cortex and adult rate of habituation both occur at about the same time in an animal's life. For example, in puppies these both occur at about 6–8 weeks (Nikitina and Novikova, 1958).

An investigation by the writer confirms the findings that immature animals habituate slowly. In this experiment 8 girls aged 4–6 years were compared with 10 young women aged 18–21 years. The subjects were stimulated with a 75 db, 500 cps tone presented through headphones at 17 sec intervals, and the PGRs recorded. Using a criterion of four successive failures of reaction, the young adults habituated in a mean of 23 trials, and all eight children failed to habituate after 60 trials, at which the experiment was concluded. Application of the nonparametric Moses' median test shows that this difference is highly significant at $P<0.005$. There was, however, no significant difference in the amplitude of the reaction.

THE ROLE OF THE ORIENTATION REACTION IN THE ACQUISITION OF MOTOR SKILLS IN CHILDREN

It is well known that young children have difficulty in acquiring and executing skilled movements such as doing up buttons, shoe laces and the like. This difficulty is attributed by Zaporozhets (1961) and his associates to the haphazard and poorly directed orientation reactions of young children. This interpretation extends the findings of Sokolov to the effect that an orientation reaction to the stimulus is necessary for the formation of a conditioned reaction. Zaporozhets argues that in the learning of a motor skill a series of orientation reactions have to be made to the successive stimulus situations which arise during the performance of the skill; it is because children cannot make adequate orientation reactions to the significant aspects of the situation that they have difficulty in acquiring the skill. In making this analysis Zaporozhets is equating the occurrence of the orientation reaction with attention and is arguing that children have difficulty in acquiring skills because they do not pay attention to the component steps in the skill. In reducing the problem of selective attention to the problem of orientation reactions in this manner it is possible that Zaporozhets has pointed the way to an advance in our understanding of the nature of attention; or, on the other hand, he may be begging quite a big question. Whether orientation reactions are an invariable concomitant of attention is a question that deserves further research.

In support of his view Zaporozhets reports several experiments in which children have been taught skills more successfully when their orientation reactions (attention) have been directed to the components of the skill. Generally, teachers put too much emphasis on the end product of the skill and thereby retard its acquisition. In one experiment involving teaching children aged 3–7 years to hammer a nail into a block of wood, children concentrating their attention on the end result took some 30–40 hits, whereas children whose attention was directed to the hand movements could achieve the result in 7 hits. In another experiment involving tracing a path correctly through a maze children did better when their orientation reactions (attention) were directed to tracing with their eyes the successive choice points along the maze than when they blundered impulsively through the maze undirected by themselves. By the time children are 5–6 years old they make these preliminary orientation investigations for themselves, but 3–4-year-olds are greatly handicapped by their impulsiveness and benefit considerably by instruction in paying attention to the components of the task.

Another question investigated by Zaporozhets is the part played by different sense modalities in the ontogenetic development of the orientation reaction. He shows that in young children up to the age of 3–4 years vision plays a relatively unimportant part and the child investigates novel objects chiefly by touch; after this, vision becomes more important and becomes the most used sense from 5–6 years onwards. However, when a completely unknown object is presented to older children they regress to tactile manipulation. The development of the ability of familiarizing oneself by visual orientation makes possible the learning of skills by imitation; so that children aged 3–4 years learn skills most rapidly by mechanically guiding their hands and learn poorly by visual imitation, whereas at the age of 6–7 years children learn more rapidly by visual imitation.

A related subject considered by Zaporozhets concerns the role of the orientation reaction in the development of the second signalling system. A number of Russian investigators have been interested in the development of the verbal control of behaviour—Pavlov's "second signalling system"—during childhood. The conclusions are that young children up to the age of about 3 or 4 years form conditioned responses like rats, needing a number of trials both for acquisition and extinction of the response, generalizing to similar stimuli, occasionally inexplicably not responding, having great difficulty with reversal shifts, etc. At about 5 to 6 years the development of language alters this and the child now conditions and extinguishes in one trial and does not generalize readily to similar stimuli.

This verbal control of behaviour, according to Zaporozhets (1961), is accomplished by conditioning (directing) orientation reactions through verbal instruction. An example of the experiments leading to this conclusion is the following. Pre-school children are conditioned to give a motor response when presented with a coloured shape against the background of another colour. When the colours are presented in different combinations it appears that children are conditioned to the figure colour rather than to the ground colour. However, children aged 5–6 years can be made to react to the ground colour by verbal instruction, whereas this is very difficult with 3- and 4-year-olds. It is inferred that the verbal instructions to look at the colour of the ground overcome the natural tendency to attend to the colour of the figure by directing the orientation reactions to the ground, and that this effect only becomes possible about the age of 5 years.

The child's visual orientation reactions to novel objects have been studied in closer detail by filming eye movements. Three stages in the reaction can be distinguished. First, there are unsystemized eye movements as the child fingers the object; from time to time he loses contact with it and he is easily distracted by extraneous stimuli. In the second stage orientation reactions to irrelevant stimuli become suppressed and the child's attention becomes concentrated more firmly on the object. At the same time there is a situation involving a sequence of events and the child can produce conditioned orientation reactions in anticipation of forthcoming occurrences. For example, in one experiment a series of light bulbs were lit up successively, and after some time when one bulb was illuminated the child gave conditioned orientation reactions to the next bulb in the sequence in advance of its illumination. This conditioning is accomplished more rapidly in older children over the age span of 3–7 years. At a later stage the name of the object evokes similar visual orientation reactions to the object itself.

PHYLOGENETIC DIFFERENCES IN THE ORIENTATION REACTION

Russian investigators have reported phylogenetic differences in the orientation reaction in a wide variety of animals, including tortoises, fish and birds as well as many species of mammals. It is generally considered that the orientation reaction is a phyletically fairly recent development, occurring in its most adequate form in primates. Some form of orientation reaction, however, can be found in all the animals mentioned above. Some of the most prominent phylogenetic differences are the following.

1. Phylogenetically more developed animals have more pronounced orientation reactions, especially in the somatic components. Thus monkeys have longer lasting reactions than dogs (Nikitina and Novikova, 1958). The orientation reactions of dogs include sharp head movements towards the stimulus, and pricking up of the ears, whereas those of carp and pigeons are more poorly adapted to the reception of the stimulus and do not include these movements (Vedyaev and Karmanova, 1958).

2. Although the reactions are more pronounced in phylogenetically more developed animals, they also habituate more rapidly to repeated stimulation. For example, Vedyaev and Karmanova (1958) presented visual and auditory stimuli to a variety of animals and reported the following number of trials to habituation:

Dogs	20	Pigeons	15–40
Rabbits	6–15	Carp	53–172
Polecats	25		

Similarly Gusel'nikov (1958) found that tortoises do not habituate their reactions after as many as 50–60 stimulations, while Zagorylko and Sollertinskaya (1958) found that it was virtually impossible to habituate the reactions of owls to visual and auditory stimuli. Among more developed animals, Nikitina and Novikova (1958) found that monkeys habituated more quickly than dogs.

3. Stimuli which are significant for the species evoke orientation reactions which are very resistant to extinction. Thus rustling noises elicit very weak and quickly habituated orientation reactions in dogs, but very powerful ones in hares, which do not habituate after as many as 240 trials. Other stimuli which are very resistant to habituation include the sight of cats for owls, the sound of wood splintering for beavers and the sound of waves splashing for fish (Klimova, 1958). There does not appear to be any clear evidence to determine whether these species, idiosyncrasies are a result of previous conditioning in the animal's life, or whether they are genetically determined.

4. The orientation reaction can be elicited more quickly after birth in more highly developed animals. In human infants the autonomic components are present in some form immediately or in the first 2 or 3 days after birth, but in dogs, cats and rabbits there is greater delay before the orientation reaction appears (Chumak, 1955; Nikitina, 1954; Nikitina and Novikova, 1958). The motor components of the orientation reaction are better developed in monkeys at the age of 3 months than they are in dogs (Nikitina and Novikova, 1958).

5. Disinhibition of a habituated stimulus cannot be obtained in pigeons and fish in the way that it can in dogs and polecats (Vedyaev and Karmanova, 1958). Disinhibition is also very rare in mammalian infants (Bronstein, Itina, Kamenetskaya and Sytova, 1958).

G

CHAPTER 7

THE ORIENTATION REACTION IN THE MEASUREMENT OF INDIVIDUAL DIFFERENCES

As is well known, Pavlov suggested three dimensions of nervous activity, which he called the strength of the nervous system, the balance or equilibrium of excitatory and inhibitory processes, and the mobility or speed with which these processes can be generated. At various times Pavlov tried to fit clinical categories and the four Hippocratic personality types (melancholics, sanguines, cholerics and phlegmatics) into this system. Thus, for example, he held that schizophrenics and melancholics had weak nervous systems. Pavlov's other conjectures, however, are apt to be self-contradictory and it is doubtful whether a logically water-tight system can be made out of them. The difficulties which Pavlov's classificatory system gives rise to have been discussed by Eysenck (1957).

Pavlov defined the strength of the nervous system in terms of the readiness with which protective ("transmarginal", "top") inhibition is generated under excessive stimulation, i.e. stimulation which may be either intense or prolonged. The generation of protective inhibition leads to atypical reactions, of which the first is the "phase of equalization" or "breaking of the law of strength"; in this stage the positive relation between stimulus and response strength breaks down and strong stimuli elicit weak responses of the same magnitude as weak stimuli. With further stimulation and the generation of more protective inhibition the paradoxical phase supervenes, in which only weak stimuli elicit a response. Finally comes the ultra-paradoxical stage, in which no response is made to positive stimuli, but negative stimuli (i.e. those to which S has been conditioned not to respond) now elicit a reaction. These various types of reaction are present in dogs following nervous breakdown, normal human beings while going to sleep, tired children, intoxicated adults and schizophrenics (Lynn, 1963).

The factor of equilibrium was regarded by Pavlov as the balance between excitatory and inhibitory processes, some individuals

90

having a predominance of the one and some of the other. The inhibition in this dimension is internal (active) inhibition, and should be clearly distinguished from the protective inhibition of the strength dimension. Internal inhibition is conceptualized as an active blocking force, so that the animal is actively checking itself from responding, whereas protective inhibition is more akin to a passive exhaustion of the nervous processes. Internal inhibition is the process responsible for experimental extinction, habituation and conditioned inhibition in discrimination learning. Pavlov therefore held that subjects who extinguish, habituate and acquire the negative reaction in discrimination learning situations quickly are characterized by a predominance of the internal inhibitory over the excitatory processes. These subjects also form positive conditioned responses slowly. Subjects with a predominance of excitation naturally display the reverse of these characteristics.

Quite a considerable volume of work has appeared in the last few years concerned with the verification and extension of Pavlov's system, both with mentally ill patients and with individual differences among normal people, and the orientation reaction has been extensively used in attempts to measure both strength and equilibrium.

THE ORIENTATION REACTION IN PATHOLOGICAL STATES

In her review of the Russian literature on this question, Vinogradova (1961) distinguishes three kinds of abnormality of the orientation reaction which have commonly been reported. These are as follows:

1. Orientation reactions which are both unusually powerful and extremely difficult to extinguish. These have been found in early acute schizophrenia, in "infectious psychosis", and in neurosis. Schizophrenics showing this pattern of orientation reaction are uncommon; in a study of 136 schizophrenics, Streltsova (1955) found only 4 who gave unusually large orientation reactions and 34 who took an abnormally large number of trials to habituate. This pattern of reaction is also found in certain patients where the cerebral cortex is damaged, notably in imbeciles and idiots, in patients with head injuries, in senility, and in alcoholics and other drug addicts.

This reaction pattern is attributed to impairment of the cerebral cortex, which has a releasing effect on the subcortex, thereby enhancing the orientation reaction size. The cortical impairment is also responsible for the retardation of inhibition. The ameliorating effects of drugs are fitted into this theoretical framework by the assumptions that caffeine restores cortical functions and that sedatives depress the reticular formation, both treatments thereby having the effect of reducing the orientation reaction and increasing its habituation rate.

2. The second type of disorder of the orientation reaction is its weakness or complete absence. This type of reaction is found in a large proportion of schizophrenics, e.g. in 65 per cent of the patients investigated by Streltsova (1955). It is also found in some mental defectives. In this reaction pattern it is assumed that the protective inhibition, which initially impairs the cortical functions leading to the enhanced orientation reactions of the first group, has now spread to the subcortex and impaired its reactivity also. The patient can be improved by any treatment which lifts the protective inhibition, and this effect can be accomplished by prolonged sleep, sedatives, stimulants, or a combination of these.

3. The third type of impairment of the orientation reaction consists of a disruption of the relation between the orientation reaction and the defensive reaction, which it will be recalled is normally elicited after a number of moderately intense stimulations which initially elicit the orientation reaction. In this type of impairment the defensive reaction occurs immediately. It has been found in some cases of "infectious psychosis" and in some schizophrenics, usually those with paranoid delusions. This reaction is regarded as a more extreme form of the weakening of the orientation reaction, resulting from more severe cortical impairment. The defensive reactions arise from the reticular formation, which is unimpaired and released from cortical control.

PERSONALITY DIFFERENCES IN THE ORIENTATION REACTION AMONG NORMAL SUBJECTS

There have been a number of rather piecemeal attempts to verify and extend Pavlov's system of individual differences, including attempts to measure the dimensions by taking indices of the orientation reaction. One such experiment is that of Voronin, Sokolov and Bao-Khua (1959). In this investigation 100 subjects were employed and were seated in sound-proof cubicles. The orientation reaction was elicited by a tone of 55 db presented 16 times at intervals of 30 to 90 sec. Ss' responses were recorded with the following measures: PGR; blocking of the alpha rhythm and of the Rolando rhythm; eye movements; forearm muscle potential (EMG); and respiration rates. All these responses tended to be elicited by the first presentation of the stimulus and to become habituated with repeated presentations, the best measures being the PGR and the blocking of the alpha rhythm, elicited on the first presentation of the stimulus in 95 per cent and 85 per cent of the subjects respectively.

Of these measures the PGR is the most satisfactory; the reaction tends to be extinguished after 7 or 8 presentations of the stimulus, but some Ss do not respond even to the first stimulus, while others continue to respond throughout the experiment. The alpha-rhythm blocking is similarly habituated with repeated stimulation, and speed of extinction of the PGR and of alpha-rhythm blocking are said to be positively correlated although no correlation is given.

In the second part of the investigation 25 Ss were used in a conditioning experiment. Ss were instructed that they would be presented with a number of stimuli, some of which would be followed by a bell. The task was to learn which stimuli were followed by the bell, and Ss were to signify that they anticipated that the stimulus would be followed by the bell by pressing a button. Six tasks of varying complexity were given, the last two being so complex that many Ss could not solve the problem after 120–180 trials. On these complex problems errors were of two sorts, namely over-reactivity (in which S pressed the button too frequently) and under-reactivity. It was noted that Ss who habituated quickly to repeated presentations of the stimulus in the first experiment tended to make errors of under-reactivity. Correlations between speed of habituation and reactivity on the two complex problems were 0·704 and 0·554. Ss who habituated quickly and made errors of under-reactivity also developed "sleep inhibition" (i.e. the EEG pattern showed waves characteristic of sleep) in the habituation of the orientation reaction experiment, but no statistical evaluation of this trend is given.

The authors interpret the results in terms of individual differences in excitatory and inhibitory processes in the nervous system. Ss

with a predominance of inhibitory processes habituated the orientation reaction quickly, developed sleep inhibition and made errors
of under-reactivity in the conditioning experiment. The reverse patterns occurred in *S*s with a predominance of excitatory processes.

THE WORK OF TEPLOV

The fullest programme of work on Pavlov's typology is that which
has been carried out by Teplov and his associates at the Academy of
Educational Science in Moscow (Teplov, 1956, 1959, 1963). Until
recently this group has tackled the problem by trying to confirm
old and discover new measures which differentiate extreme groups,
as defined by some known criterion. It has now become recognized,
however, that this is a problem most satisfactorily solved by factor
analysis of a large number of measures, and two such studies have
appeared. Both factor analytic studies include orientation reaction
measures among the variables recorded and are thus of interest
from the point of view of the correlates of the orientation reaction.

The first factor analysis is that of Rozhdestvenskaya, Nebylitsin,
Borisova and Ermolaeva-Tomina (1960). The following measures
were recorded from 40 subjects:

1. Generation of Protective Inhibition. It is assumed, following
Pavlov, that continuous stimulation leads to the generation of
protective inhibition and that this development occurs more quickly
in subjects with weak nervous systems. The procedure involves the
conditioned photochemical reaction.

The subject is first dark adapted and his absolute visual threshold
measured. A flash of light is then presented, which has the effect of
lowering the subject's sensitivity; this lowering of sensitivity is then
conditioned by pairing a visual stimulus with the flash. But with
continued reinforced trials there is an extinction with reinforcement
effect in that the conditioned stimulus has less and less effect. This
extinction with reinforcement effect is attributed to the generation
of protective inhibition following intense stimulation, and consequently occurs sooner in individuals with weak nervous systems.
The measure is the degree of weakening of the strength of the
conditioned reaction with continuous reinforcement. A detailed
description of this method has been published by this group in
English (Nebylitsin, Rozhdestvenskaya and Teplov, 1960).

2. The same procedure, except that the subjects are given 0·2 gr

of caffeine. It is assumed that caffeine has the effect of weakening the nervous system.

3. First Induction method. The subject is dark adapted and his absolute visual threshold measured. A low intensity visual stimulus is now presented briefly and this has the effect of lowering *S*s' threshold, an effect attributed to the irradiation of excitation. As the intensity of this flash is raised there comes a point at which it *raises* instead of lowering the absolute threshold. This is termed the threshold of the concentration of excitation, since it is assumed that the flash sets up a centre of excitation in which the excitatory processes are concentrated, thereby reducing the excitatory processes in other cortical areas. The intensity at which the additional flash raises the absolute threshold is called "the threshold of the concentration of excitation". The measure taken is this threshold, and it is lower in weak nervous system subjects.

4, 5, 6. Second, Third and Fourth Induction methods. The subject's visual threshold is first measured and then measured again in the presence of an additional stimulus 100 times more intense than *S*s' threshold. The additional stimulus brings about a rise in the absolute threshold, attributed to the concentration of excitation process described above. This decrease in sensitivity is expressed as a percentage of the initial level of sensitivity; this percentage may be called P_1. Special stresses are now imposed on the subject. For this measure S is fatigued by being required to give 20 threshold measurements at 1-min intervals. For measure 5, S is given 8 trials of exposure of the test stimulus plus the additional stimulus. For measure 6, S is given 0·2 gr of caffeine.

After these various stresses, the procedure is repeated and a second percentage fall in sensitivity is obtained: P_2. The final measure is the ratio of P_1 to P_2, and it is assumed that the stresses will have a greater effect on subjects with weak nervous systems.

7. Absolute visual thresholds. It is assumed that subjects with strong nervous systems have high thresholds.

8. Effect of 0·2 gr of caffeine on absolute visual thresholds. In strong nervous systems the threshold is unaffected or slightly lowered. In weak nervous systems the threshold is either considerably lowered or raised.

9. Photochemical conditioned reflex: the same measure as 1, except that an auditory conditioned stimulus is used instead of a visual one.

10. Photochemical conditioned reflex: the same measure as 1, after the subject has taken 0·2 gr of caffeine.

11. Absolute auditory threshold. Strong nervous systems have high thresholds.

12. Effect of 0·2 gr of caffeine on absolute auditory thresholds. In strong nervous systems the threshold is unaffected or slightly lowered. In weak nervous systems the threshold is considerably lowered or raised.

13. Ergographic method. The subject is required to lift and let fall rhythmically a weight on an ergograph, and on presentation of a visual signal must lift it as high as possible. On test trials the subject is given caffeine, which was assumed to have the effect of weakening the reaction in weak nervous system subjects. The measure taken was the degree of fall off in the response strength after caffeine. However, this measure and three succeeding variations of the ergographic method did not correlate with the other measures of the strength of the nervous system, and have consequently been rejected as suitable tests in their present form.

14. Ergographic method: as in 13, except that the subject is now weakened by continuous performance instead of by caffeine.

15. Ergographic method: as in 13, except that an auditory signal is used.

16. Ergographic method: as in 14, except that an auditory signal is used.

17. Orientation Reaction Extinction: number of trials necessary for extinction of the orientation reaction (measuring the vaso-reaction) to a visual stimulus.

18. Orientation Reaction Size: size of the initial vaso-reaction to the visual stimulus.

19. Orientation Reaction Extinction: number of trials to habituation of the vaso-reaction to an auditory stimulus.

20. Orientation Reaction Size: size of the initial vaso-reaction to the visual stimulus.

21. Intersensory Effects: the absolute visual threshold is measured and an auditory stimulus is presented. The effect of an extraneous stimulus can be to raise or lower the absolute threshold according to circumstances: the very extensive Soviet work in this area has been reviewed by London (1954). According to Teplov and his associates, the auditory stimulus lowers absolute visual thresholds in strong nervous system subjects and raises them in weak nervous system subjects.

These measures are described and discussed in detail by Gray (1964). The intercorrelations between these 21 variables are shown in Table 1, and the results of the factor analysis in Table 2.

TABLE 1

Variables	1	2	3	4	5	6	7	8	9	10	11	12	13	14	15	16	17	18	19	20
1																				
2	61																			
3	54	49																		
4	45	46	55																	
5	56	31	52	55																
6	69	31	59	73	53															
7	49	68	45	44	41	42														
8	58	56	42	59	35	46	58													
9	41	48	23	24	26	18	32	43												
10	31	61	26	25	22	19	39	40	85											
11	17	27	42	45	24	37	34	20	33	37										
12	24	40	13	22	10	16	51	22	35	44	33									
13	04	15	10	13	16	21	42	22	-20	-18	12	10								
14	06	03	00	-08	05	-05	-04	-23	15	-12	-08	-20	26							
15	02	-21	10	16	-17	14	04	-06	-11	-15	07	28	01	-01						
16	01	11	15	-07	08	04	07	02	28	05	01	-15	10	27	-22					
17	26	00	30	04	16	-07	05	05	37	26	27	12	-17	24	-09	02				
18	22	14	27	07	25	-15	08	24	29	26	17	12	22	17	-04	00	85			
19	10	-19	28	06	13	-20	-17	-08	04	-02	19	12	-22	15	13	-07	65	51		
20	09	-13	19	-22	29	-28	-15	-33	-07	-08	-01	-13	-42	26	-04	07	47	29	43	
21	32	33	29	42	29	43	30	23	30	26	25	33	31	-21	09	21	04	-25	-23	-32

It will be seen from inspection of the tables that the measures 1 to 12 and 21 intercorrelate well and have high loadings on the first factor, which is interpreted as the strength of the nervous system. These are all measures of thresholds of one sort or another and the size of the correlations obtained between them is undoubtedly impressive. The attempt to devise a work-fatigue measure (the ergographic methods, measures 13–16) of the strength of the nervous system was not a success.

The orientation reaction measures do not correlate with the strength measures but correlate well among themselves and have high loadings on the second factor. The authors interpret this factor as equilibrium, subjects with high excitatory processes showing large orientation reactions and resistance to extinction.

The second factor analysis involving the orientation reaction is that of Nebylitsin (1963). This experiment was principally concerned with finding intercorrelating measures of equilibrium, and the

TABLE 2

	Factors					
Variables	Before rotation			After rotation		
	I	II	III	I	II	III
1	71	09	−10	71	12	−08
2	67	17	−37	69	−07	36
3	69	−08	−29	64	33	−22
4	70	26	−23	74	−01	−24
5	56	−07	−27	52	27	−21
6	64	38	−30	74	−20	−35
7	70	32	17	76	−15	14
8	65	28	17	70	−13	14
9	65	−32	57	54	34	66
10	59	−17	59	52	18	65
11	53	−07	−05	49	21	00
12	47	18	17	50	−09	12
13	28	30	−14	35	−18	−18
14	04	−29	−15	−04	31	−08
15	03	19	−27	08	−11	−30
16	07	−24	20	00	19	25
17	39	−73	−22	18	83	−03
18	42	−59	−11	25	69	05
19	15	−59	−34	−01	67	−19
20	−06	−66	−25	−23	65	−10
21	43	41	−06	52	−25	−12

relationship of these to measures of strength. Most of the measures of equilibrium are derived from Pavlov's theory that subjects with predominant excitatory processes condition quickly but extinguish slowly and have difficulty in not responding to the negative stimulus in discrimination learning situations and in forming delayed conditioned reactions. Measures were derived from EEG experiments on 22 subjects, the measures taken being as follows:

1. Alpha Index: it was expected that subjects with predominant excitation would have a relatively little amount of alpha rhythm. The measure is the proportion of alpha rhythm to all other rhythms.

2. Alpha Amplitude: it was assumed that subjects with predominant excitation would have low amplitude alpha rhythms.

3. Frequency of alpha rhythms: it was assumed that subjects with predominant excitation would have high frequency alpha rhythms.

4. Orientation Reaction Size: it was assumed that subjects with

predominant excitation would show large orientation reactions. The measure taken was the duration of alpha blocking to the first presentation of the auditory stimulus (a 300 cps, 70 db tone).

5. Orientation Reaction Extinction: it was assumed that subjects with predominant excitation would give a large number of reactions before extinction. The measure was the number of responses to the auditory stimulus.

6. Orientation Reaction Size: duration of the alpha-blocking reaction to the first presentation of a visual stimulus (a light of 40 lux).

The next four variables are derived from an experiment in which the alpha-blocking reaction to light is conditioned to an auditory stimulus. The auditory CS lasted 4 sec and the visual UCS began 1 sec after the presentation of the CS. Both stimuli ended together. Intervals between trials varied from 20 to 30 sec. This experiment gave the next four variables.

7. Duration of alpha blocking: it was assumed that subjects with predominant excitation would show greater durations of alpha blocking. The measure was the average duration in the first 10 trials.

8. Duration of conditioned alpha blocking: it was assumed that subjects with predominant excitation would condition quickly. The measure was the average duration of conditioned alpha blocking over the first 8 trials.

9. Duration of conditioned alpha blocking after a series of pictures had been presented to the subject. It was assumed that this would arouse the subject and enhance the conditioned alpha blocking, and that this would occur to a greater extent in subjects with predominant excitation. The measure was the average duration of conditioned alpha blocking over 3 trials after the presentation of the pictures.

10. Extinction of conditioned alpha blocking: it was assumed that subjects with predominant excitation would be slow to extinguish the conditioned reaction. The measure was the number of trials to extinction.

11. Discrimination Learning. It is assumed that subjects with predominant excitation will be slow in learning not to respond to the negative stimulus in discrimination learning, since this process involves inhibition. The subject was required to discriminate a negative stimulus of 250 cps from the original positive stimulus

of 300 cps. The measure was the number of trials to achieve the discrimination.

12. Extinction with reinforcement. This effect is attributed, as in the previous factor analysis, to the generation of protective inhibition with repeated stimulation, and it is assumed that this occurs sooner in the weak nervous system. The extinction with reinforcement effect is obtained when the last conditioned responses are weaker than the first, and this difference constituted the measure.

13. Extinction with reinforcement. The same measure with a higher intensity auditory stimulus, which produces the extinction with reinforcement effect more quickly.

14. Extinction with reinforcement. The same measure again when the subject has been given caffeine, which also produces the extinction with reinforcement effect more quickly.

15. Absolute auditory threshold. This was established in the first factor analysis as a good measure of strength and is introduced here as a marker variable.

16. Acquisition of Delayed Conditioned Response: Anticipatory Errors. Pavlov assumed that inhibitory processes intervene in delayed conditioning to check the appearance of the response during the delay period. Hence subjects in whom excitatory processes predominate should have difficulty in delayed conditioning. This was tested by the same conditioned alpha-blocking procedure as used in the earlier experiments, except that a 6-sec interval was introduced between the onset of the conditioned auditory stimulus and the unconditioned visual stimulus. It was assumed that subjects in whom excitatory processes predominated would make anticipatory errors and this variable is a measure of this tendency.

17. Acquisition of Delayed Conditioned Response: Preliminary Conditioning. The first criterion of successful delayed conditioning was when the response occurred in the delay period but in anticipation of the onset of the unconditioned stimulus. This is regarded as a step towards successful delayed conditioning and is expected to occur sooner in subjects with a predominance of inhibitory processes.

18. Final Acquisition of Delayed Conditioned Response. The number of trials for perfect delayed conditioning. It is naturally assumed that subjects with predominant inhibition will achieve this first.

The intercorrelations between these 18 measures are shown in Table 3, and results of the factor analysis after rotation in Table 4.

It will be observed that quite a considerable measure of success has been achieved in finding 14 measures of equilibrium (variables 1–11 and 16–18) and 4 of strength (variables 12–15), and that the two

TABLE 3

Variables	1	2	3	4	5	6	7	8	9	10	11	12	13	14	15	16	17
1																	
2	60																
3	−37	−17															
4	−54	−33	45														
5	−64	−21	56	65													
6	−45	−38	39	58	50												
7	−47	−35	52	48	54	85											
8	−61	−31	56	72	66	69	79										
9	−18	−13	29	62	04	31	34	37									
10	−45	−10	32	45	76	58	63	53	17								
11	−24	−26	29	48	44	43	39	28	14	42							
12	−28	−36	20	22	37	03	09	19	11	−17	31						
13	−04	−40	33	20	07	−14	−04	21	06	−14	17	54					
14	−48	−39	33	10	18	47	65	54	25	06	−07	31	−01				
15	−39	−12	33	26	17	19	38	27	41	13	27	63	27	20			
16	−51	−38	33	62	61	56	51	45	39	50	64	36	15	19	42		
17	−57	−39	35	3	56	27	11	16	18	45	39	−06	00	05	−10	32	
18	−31	−34	20	−02	07	15	03	−12	−10	14	07	−25	−21	−17	−10	−14	69

TABLE 4

Variables	Factors			
	I	II	III	IV
1	−62	−15	−37	32
2	−56	09	−26	−51
3	50	18	40	10
4	76	02	21	30
5	85	−09	14	15
6	59	−20	61	00
7	50	−12	74	10
8	57	01	68	28
9	31	15	32	22
10	72	−39	18	08
11	69	14	−10	05
12	40	59	03	−37
13	28	51	−01	42
14	03	14	79	−13
15	30	60	19	18
16	74	20	11	16
17	69	−17	−09	−50
18	23	−22	−03	−66

dimensions appear substantially independent. Nebylitsin interprets factor III as alpha reactivity and does not attempt to interpret factor IV.

A further study concerned with the orientation reaction as a measure of the equilibrium of the nervous system has been reported by Rozhdestvenskaya (1963). In this investigation 25 subjects were tested on six measures:

1. Orientation reaction size: the finger vaso-constriction reaction was measured, taking the average amplitude of the first 10 trials.

2. Orientation reaction latency: the average latency of the same reactions.

3. Speed of conditioning: the subject was conditioned to produce vaso-constriction to an auditory stimulus, the unconditioned stimulus being cold. Three successive vaso-reactions to the CS was taken as the criterion of successful conditioning.

4. Adaptive vaso-reactions to cold: average amplitude of the first 10 reactions.

5. Latency of the adaptive vaso-reactions to cold: average of the first 10 reactions.

6. Stability of the resting level plethysmograph.

It was assumed that subjects with predominant excitation would show large orientation reactions and extinguish them slowly; they would also condition quickly, and have high amplitude and low latency adaptive reactions. These subjects would in addition have an unstable plethysmographic resting level. The correlation coefficients between the measures were not calculated, but examination of the results shows that the orientation reaction habituation rates, speed of conditionability, and the stability of the resting level plethysmograph hang together well, i.e. subjects differentiated on one measure have markedly different scores on the others. On the other hand the size of the orientation reaction and adaptive reaction did not differentiate the subjects.

A final investigation which reports findings rather similar to those of Rozhdestvenskaya is presented by Ermolaeva-Tomina (1963). This experiment was carried out on 14 subjects and involved the following tests:

1. PGR amplitude to auditory and visual stimuli.

2. Habituation rates of the PGR with repeated stimulation.

3. Speed of conditioning. The procedure involved pressing a dynamometer at the onset of a light (UCS). The response was

conditioned by presenting a 1100 cps tone (CS) 4 sec before the onset of the UCS.

4. Discrimination learning. After the conditioned reaction had been acquired, S was required to discriminate the CS from a negative stimulus of 60 cps.

5. Reversal shift. The positive and negative stimuli in the discrimination learning were then reversed, so that S had to respond to the negative stimulus and not to the positive stimulus.

The intercorrelations of these measures were not calculated but were examined to see how far they held together in the expected directions. It was found that one group of subjects habituated slowly, conditioned quickly, discriminated the negative stimulus slowly and in the reversal shift tended to make errors of over-reactivity. This group of subjects is regarded as having predominant excitation and the others, who show the reverse of these characteristics, as having predominant inhibition. As in Rozhdestvenskaya's results, the size of the orientation reaction did not differentiate the two groups.

There can be no doubt that the Teplov group has achieved considerable success in discovering highly intercorrelating measures of these two dimensions of nervous activity. Western investigators of individual differences may well benefit from considering the possibility of integrating the Russian findings with their own work. One possibility discussed briefly by Nebylitsin is that the "strength of the nervous system" corresponds to anxiety, subjects with weak nervous systems being anxious. This correspondence would be in line with the tendency of "weak" subjects to suffer nervous breakdowns. There is, however, very little evidence on the question of how far anxiety is related to the various threshold measures devised by Teplov and his associates and this is a question well worth investigation.

Another possible correspondence is that between equilibrium and Eysenck's (1957) dimension of introversion – extraversion, which Eysenck has himself identified with the balance of excitatory and inhibition processes. There are at least two measures common to equilibrium and introversion – extraversion. One is conditionability, individuals with predominant excitation (Teplov, 1959) and introverts (Eysenck, 1957), showing speedy conditioning and slow extinction. The other is the alpha index, which is low in individuals with predominant excitation (Nebylitsin, 1963) and also in introverts

(Claridge and Herrington, 1963). On the other hand, the Hull – Eysenck construct of reactive inhibition, differences in which are assumed to underlie the introversion – extraversion dimension, remains closely related to Pavlov's original conception of internal inhibition in that it is a fatigue-like process; while the Russians themselves have modified this conception, as outlined in Chapter 4. There is considerable scope for a research programme to integrate these two systems.

REFERENCES

(References in Russian are given in English translation)

ADEY, W. R., MERRILLEES, N. C. R. and SUNDERLAND, S. (1956). The entorhinal area; behavioural, evoked potential, and histological studies of its relationships with brain-stem regions *Brain*, **79**, 414–439.

ADEY, W. R., MERRILLEES, N. C. R. and SUNDERLAND, S. (1957). Corticifugal influences on intrinsic brain stem conduction in cat and monkey. *J. Neurophysiol.*, **20**, 1–16.

AFFANNI, J., MARCHIAFAVA, P. L. and ZERNICKI, B. (1962). Orientation reactions in the midpontine pretrigeminal cat. *Arch. Ital. Biol.*, **100**, 297–304.

AKERT, K., KOELLA, W. P. and HESS, R. (1952). Sleep produced by electrical stimulation of the thalamus. *Amer. J. Physiol.*, **168**, 260–267.

ANOKHIN, P. K. (1958). *The Role of the Orientation Reaction in Conditioning, the Orientation Reaction and Orienting-Investigating Activity.* Moscow: Acad. Pedag. Sciences, R.S.F.S.R.

APELBAUM, J., SILVA, E. N. and FRICK, O. (1959). Frequency discrimination and "arousal" reaction 18. *XXI International Congress of Physiological Sciences.* Buenos Aires, 9–15.

ARTEMIEV, V. V. (1951). Electrical responses of the cerebral cortex to acoustic stimuli in anaesthetized and unanaesthetized animals. *J. Physiol. U.S.S.R.*, **37**, 688–702.

BAUMGARTEN, R. VON, MOLLICA, A. and MORUZZI, G. (1954). Modulierung der Entladungsfrequenz einzelner Zellen der substantia reticularis durch corticofugale und cerebellare Impulse. *Pflügers Arch. ges. Physiol.*, **259**, 56–78.

BECK, E. C., DOTY, R. W. and KWI, K. A. (1958). Electrocortical reactions associated with conditioned flexion reflexes. *EEG Clin. Neurophysiol.*, **10**, 279–289.

BENOIT, O. (1958). Étude des variations de l'activation corticale provoquée par des stimulations réticulaires en expérience chronique. *J. Physiol. Paris*, **50**, 153–155.

BERLYNE, D. E. (1958a). The influence of albedo and complexity of stimuli on visual fixation in the human infant. *Brit. J. Psychol.*, **49**, 315–318.

BERLYNE, D. E. (1958b). The influence of complexity and novelty in visual figures on orienting responses. *J. exp. Psychol.*, **55**, 289–296.

BERLYNE, D. E. (1960). *Conflict, Arousal and Curiosity.* New York: McGraw-Hill.

BERLYNE, D. E. (1961). Conflict and the orientation reaction. *J. exp. Psychol.*, **62**, 476–483.

BIRUKOV, G. (1951). Ermudung und Umstimmung bei Gleichgewichts-reaktionen der Amphiben. *Verhandl. deutsch. Zool. Gesellsch. Wilhelmshaven. Zoologischer Anzeiger Suppl.*, **16**, 1952.

BIRYUKOV, D. A. (1958). The nature of orienting reactions. In L. G. VORONIN *et al.* (Eds.), *The Orienting Reflex and Orienting-Investigating Activity.* Moscow: Acad. Pedag. Sciences.

BONVALLET, M., DELL, P. and HIEBEL, G. (1954). Tonus sympathique et activité électrique corticale. *EEG Clin. Neurophysiol.*, **6**, 119–144.

BRADLEY, P. B. (1957). The central action of certain drugs in relation to the reticular formation of the brain. In H. H. JASPER *et al.* (Eds.), *Reticular Formation of the Brain*. London: Churchill.

BRANDT, H. F. (1944). *The Science of Seeing*. New York: Philosophical Library.

BREMER, F. (1954). The neurophysiological problem of sleep. In ADRIAN, E. D., BREMER, F. and JASPER, H. (Eds.), *Brain Mechanisms and Consciousness*. Oxford: Blackwell.

BREMER, F. and STOUPEL, N. (1959). Facilitation et inhibition des potentiels évoqués corticaux dans l'éveil cérébral. *Arch. init. Physiol.*, **67**, 240–275.

BRIDGER, W. H. and REISER, M. F. (1959). Psychophysiological studies of the neonate: and approach toward the methodological and theoretical problems involved. *Psychosom. Med.*, **21**, 265–276.

BRIULLOVA, S. V. (1958). On some peculiarities of the orientation reaction in people who have undergone closed traumata of the cerebral cortex and persons suffering from neuroses. In L. G. VORONIN *et al.* (Eds.), *The Orientation Reaction and Exploratory Behaviour*. Moscow: Acad. Pedag. Sciences.

BRODAL, A. (1957). The Reticular Formation of the Brain Stem. Anatomical Aspects and Functional correlations. Edinburgh: Oliver & Boyd.

BRONSTEIN, A. I., ITINA, N. A., KAMENETSKAYA, H. G. and SYTOVA, V. A. (1958). *Orientating Reactions in Newborn Babies. The Orientation Reaction and Orientating Investigating Activity*. Moscow: Acad. Pedag. Sciences. R.S.F.S.R.

BYKOV, V. D. (1958). On the dynamic of the orientating investigating reaction during the formation of positive and in inhibitory conditioned reactions and their alternation. *The Orientation Reaction and Orienting-Investigating Activity*. Moscow: Acad. Pedag. Sciences. R.S.F.S.R.

CASPERS, H. (1955). Forderung und Hemmung von Narcotica Wirkungen auf das Zentral-nerven System durch elektrische Stammhirnreizungen mit verschiedenen Reinzgrossen. *Ztschr. ges. exper. Med.*, **125**, 386–400.

CASPERS, H. and WINKEL, K. (1954). Die Beeflussung der Grosshirnrinden-rhythmik durch Reizungen im Zwischen und Mittelhirn bei der Ratte. *Pflügers Arch. ges. Physiol.*, **259**, 334–356.

CASPERS, H., LERCHE, E. and GRÜTER, H. (1958). Adaptationserscheinungen der akustisch ausgelosten Weckreaktion bei Reizung mit definierten Tonimpulsen. *Pflügers Arch. ges. Physiol.*, **267**, 128–141.

CHANG, H.-T. (1960). Some observations on the excitability changes of cortical and subcortical neurons and their possible significance in the process of conditioning. In H. JASPER and G. D. SMIRNOV (Eds.), the Moscow Colloquium on Electroencephalography of Higher Nervous Activity. *EEG Clin. Neurophysiol.*, Suppl. 13.

CHUMAK, V. I. (1955). On the extinction of the orientating reaction in the early post-natal period. *Pavlov J. Higher Nerv. Act.*, **5**, 6.

CLARIDGE, G. S. and HERRINGTON, R. N. (1963). An EEG correlate of the Archimedes spiral after-effect and its relationship with personality. *Behav. Res. Ther.*, **1**, 217–229.

DARROW, C. W. (1936). The galvanic skin reflex (sweating) and blood pressure as preparatory and facilitative functions. *Psychol. Bull.*, **33**, 73–94.

DAVIS, R. C. (1957). Response patterns. *Trans. N.Y. Acad. Sci.*, **19**, 731–739.

DAVIS, R. C., BUCKWALD, A. M. and FRANKMANN, R. W. (1955). *Autonomic and Muscular Responses and their Relation to Simple Stimuli*. Psychol. Monogr. No. 405.

DEGTYAR, E. N. (1963). Conditions required for the formation of a CR system at various functional levels of children's nervous activity. *Zhur. Vysshei Nerv. Deiatel.*, **13**, 631–637.

DELL, P., BONVALLET, M. and HUGELIN, A. (1961). Mechanisms of reticular deactivation. In G. E. W. WOLSTENHOLME and M. O'CONNOR (Eds.), *The Nature of Sleep*. London: Churchill.

DUMONT, S. and DELL, P. (1958). Facilitations spécifiques et non-spécifiques des responses visuelles corticales. *J. Physiol. (Paris)*, **50**, 261–264.

ERMOLAEVA-TOMINA, L. B. (1963). On the question of the use of the P.G.R. index for determining nervous system type in man. In B. M. TREPLOV (Ed.), *Typological Characteristics of Higher Nervous Activity in Man*. Vol. 3. Moscow: Acad. Pedag. Sciences, R.S.F.S.R.

EYSENCK, H. J. (1957). *The Dynamics of Anxiety and Hysteria*. London: Routledge & Kegan Paul.

FANTZ, R. L. (1958a). Pattern vision in young infants. *Psychol. Rec.*, **8**, 43–48.

FANTZ, R. L. (1958b). Visual discrimination in a neonate chimpanzee. *Perc. Mot. Skills*, **8**, 59–66.

FAVALE, E., LOEB, C., ROSSI, G. F., and SACCO, G. (1959), *XXI Int. physiol. Congr. Abstracts*, p. 87.

FRENCH, J. D. (1957). Corticifugal connections with the reticular formation. In H. H. JASPER et al. (Eds.), *Reticular Formation of the Brain*. London: Churchill.

FUSTER, J. M. (1957). Tachistoscopic perception in monkeys. *Fed. Proc.*, **16**, 43.

GALAMBOS, R., SHEATZ, G. and VERNIER, V. G. (1956). Electrophysiological correlates of conditioned responses in cat. *Science*, **123**, 367–377.

GAMBURG, A. L. (1958). Orienting and defensive reactions in simple and paranoid forms of schizophrenia. In L. G. VORONIN et al. (Eds.), *The Orientation Reaction and Orienting-Investigating Activity*. Moscow: Acad. Pedag. Sciences. R.S.F.S.R.

GASTAUT, H. (1957). The role of the reticular formation in establishing conditioned reactions. In *Reticular Formation of the Brain*, W. H. JASPER, Boston: Little, Brown.

GASTAUT, H. and BERT, J. (1961). Electroencephalographic detection of sleep induced by repetitive sensory stimuli. In G. E. W. WOLSTENHOLME and M. O'CONNOR (Eds.), *The Nature of Sleep*. London: Churchill.

GASTAUT, H. and ROGER, A. (1960). Les mécanismes de l'activité nerveuse supérieure au niveau des grandes structures fonctionelles du cerveau. In H. H. JASPER and G. D. SMIRNOV (Eds.), Moscow Colloquium on Electroencephalogy of Higher Nervous Activities. *EEG Clin. Neurophysiol.*, Suppl. 13.

GASTAUT, H., VIGOUROUX, R. and NAQUET, R. (1952). Comportements posturaux et cinétiques provoquées par stimulation sous-corticale chez le chat non anesthésié; leur relation avec le "reflex d'orientation". *J. Psychologie*, **4**, 257–271.

GERSHUNDI, G. V., KOZHEVNIKOV, V. A., MARUSEVA, A. M., AVAKYAN, R. V., RADIONOVA, E. A., ALTMAN, J. A. and SOROKO, V. I. (1960). Modifications in electrical responses of the auditory system in different states of higher nervous activity. In H. H. JASPER and G. D. SMIRNOV (Eds.), The Moscow Colloquium on Electroencephalography of Higher Nervous Activity. *EEG. Clin. Neurophysiol.*, Suppl. 13.

GLICKMAN, S. E. and FELDMAN, S. M. (1960). Habituation to direct stimulation of the reticular formation. *Federation Proc.*, **19**, 288.

GRANIT, R. (1955). *Receptors and Sensory Perception*. New Haven: Yale Univ. Press.

GRASTYAN, E. (1959). The hippocampus and higher nervous activity. In M. A. BRAZIER (Ed.), *The Central Nervous System and Behaviour*. New York: J. Macy.

GRASTYAN, E. (1961). The significance of the earliest manifestations of conditioning in the mechanism of learning. In A. FESSARD *et al.* (Eds.), *Brain Mechanisms and Learning*. Oxford: Blackwell.

GRASTYAN, E., LISSAK, K. and SZABO, J. (1954). Funktionelle Zusammenhange zwischen den Hemmungs und Activierungssystem des Grosshirns. *Acta physiol. Hung. Suppl.*, **6**, 29.

GRASTYAN, E., LISSAK, K. and SZABO, J. (1955). Cortical electrical manifestations of diencephalic inhibition. *Acta physiol. Hung.*, **7**, 187–198.

GRAY, J. A. (1964) *Pavlov's Typology*. Oxford: Pergamon Press.

GROSSMAN, R. G. and WANG, S. C. (1956). Thalamic inhibition of subcortically induced locomotor movements. *Fed. Proc.* **15**, 83.

GUSEL'NIKOV, V. I. (1958). The expression of the orientation reaction in the oscillations of the biolectric potentials of the frontal lobes of fish, tortoises and pigeons. *The Orientation Reaction and Orienting-Investigating Activity*. Moscow: Acad. Pedag. Sciences. R.S.F.S.R.

HERNÁNDEZ-PEÓN, R. (1960). Neurophysiological correlates of habituation and other manifestations of plastic inhibition (Internal inhibition). In H. H. JASPER and G. D. SMIRNOV (Eds.), The Moscow Colloquium on Electroencephalography and Clinical Neurophysiology. *EEG Clin. Neurophysiol.*, Suppl. 13.

HERNÁNDEZ-PEÓN, R. and BRUST-CARMONA, H. (1961). Functional role of subcortical structures in habituation and conditioning. In A. FESSARD *et al.* (Eds.), *Brain Mechanisms and Learning*. Oxford: Blackwell.

HERNÁNDEZ-PEÓN, R., JOUVET, M. and SCHERRER, H. (1957). Auditory potentials at cochlear nucleus during acoustic habituation. *Acta neurol. latinoamer.*, **3**, 144–156.

HERNÁNDEZ-PEÓN, R. and SCHERRER, H. (1955). Habituation to acoustic stimuli in cochlear nucleus. *Fed. Proc.*, **14**, 71.

HERNÁNDEZ-PEÓN, R., SCHERRER, H., and JOUVET, M. (1956). Modification of electrical activity in cochlear nucleus during "attention" in unanaesthetised cats. *Science*, **123**, 331–332.

HESS, W. R. (1944). Das Schlafsyndrom als Folge dienzephaler Reizung. *Helv. Physiol. Acta*, **2**, 305–344.

HESS, W. R. (1949). *Das Zwischenhirn, Syndrome, Lokalizationen, Funktionen.* Basel: Schwabe.

HESS, W. R. (1954). The diencephalic sleep centre. In ADRIAN, E. D. *et al.* (Eds.), *Brain Mechanism and Consciousness*. Oxford: Blackwell.

HUBEL, D., HENSON, C., RUPERT, A. and GALAMBOS, R. (1959). "Attention" units in the auditory cortex. *Science*, **129**, 1279–1280.

HUGELIN, A. and BONVALLET, M. (1957). Tonus corticale et contrôle de la facilitation motrice d'origine réticulaire. *J. Physiol.*, Paris, **48**, 1171–1200.

INGVAR, D. and SÖDERBERG, U. (1958). Cortical blood flow related to EEG patterns evoked by stimulation of the brain stem. *Acta physiol. scand.*, **42**, 130–143.

JACOBSON, J. H. and GESTRING, G. I. (1958). Centrifugal influence upon the electroretinogram. *A.M.A. Arch. Ophthalmol.* **60**, 295–302.

JASPER, H. H. (1957). Recent advances in our understanding of ascending activities of the reticular system. In H. H. JASPER *et al.* (Eds.), *Reticular Formation of the Brain*. London: Churchill.

JOHN, E. R. and KILLAM, K. F. (1960). Studies of electrical activity of brain during differential conditioning in cats. In J. WORTIS (Ed.), *Recent Advances in Biological Psychiatry*. New York: Grune & Stratton.

JONES, H. E. (1930). The galvanic skin reflex in infancy. *Child. Developm.*, **1**, 106–110.

JOUVET, M. (1961). Récherches sur les mécanismes neurophysiologiques du sommeil et de l'apprentissage négatif. In A. FESSARD *et al.* (Eds.), *Brain Mechanisms and Learning*. Oxford: Blackwell.

JOUVET, M., BENOIT, C. and COURJON, J. (1956). EEG studies of the processes of connection formation between a light stimulus and a sound stimulus in the cat. *EEG Clin. Neurophysiol.*, **8**, 727–728.

JUNG, R. (1957). Tierexperimentelle Grundlagen und EEG–Untersuchungen bei neurologische Erkrankungen. *1. intern. neurol. Congress*, Brussels.

JUNG, R. (1961). In *Sensory Communication*, Ed. ROSENBLITH, W. A. MIT Press; J. Wiley, New York and London.

JUS, A. and JUS, C. (1960). Étude de l'extinction par répétition de l'expression EEG du réflexe d'orientation et de l'action du frein externe sur les réactions EEG aux différents stimuli chez l'homme. In H. H. JASPER and G. D. SMIRNOV (Eds.), Moscow Colloquium on Electroencephalography and Higher Nervous Activity. *EEG clin. Neurophysiol.*, Suppl. 13.

KASATKIN, N. I., MIRZOYANTS, N. S. and KHOKHITVA, J. (1953). Orientation conditioned reflexes in infants during the first year of life. PAVLOV, J. *Higher Nerv. Act.*, **3**, 192–202.

KAZMIIN, G. I. and FEDOROV, V. K. (1951). *14th Conference on Problems of Higher Nervous Activity*. Moscow and Leningrad.

KEY, B. J. and BRADLEY, P. B. (1960). The effects of drugs on conditioning and habituation to arousal stimuli in animals. *Psychopharmologia*, **1**, 450–462.

KLIMOVA, V. I. (1958). The properties of the components of some orientation reactions. *The Orientation Reaction and Orienting-Investigating Activity*. Moscow: Acad. Pedag. Sciences. R.S.F.S.R.

KOCH, E. (1932). Die Irradiation der pressorezeptorischen Kreislaufreflex. *Klin. Wschr.*, **2**, 225–227.

KONORSKI, J. M. (1948). *Conditioned Reflexes and Neuron Organization*. London: Cambridge University Press.

KONORSKI, J. M. (1960). Discussion of Gastaut and Roger's Mécanismes de l'activité nerveuse supérieure. In H. H. JASPER and G. D. SMIRNOV (Eds.), The Moscow Colloquium on Electroencephalography and Higher Nervous Activity. *EEG Clin. Neurophysiol.*, Suppl. 13.

LACEY, J. I. (1959). Interpolated remark in Grastyan's The hippocampus and higher nervous activity. M. A. BRAZIER (Ed.), *The Central Nervous System and Behaviour*. New York: J. Macy.

LAGUTINA, N. I. (1955). Proceedings of the All-Union Congress of Psychologists, Biochemists and Pharmacologists. Moscow.

LANDIS, C. and HUNT, W. A. (1939). *The Startle Pattern*. New York: Farrar & Rinehart.

LANSING, R. W., SCHWARTZ, E. and LINDSLEY, D. B. (1959). Reaction time and EEG activation under alerted and nonalerted conditions. *J. exp. Psychol.*, **58**, 1–7.

LETTVIN, J. Y., MATURANA, H. R., PITTS, W. H. and McCULLOCH, W. S. (1961). In *Sensory Communication*, ROSENBLITH (Ed.), W. A. MIT Press; J. Wiley, New York and London.

LIDDELL, H. S. (1959). Interpolated remark in Grastyan's The hippocampus and higher nervous activity. In M. A. BRAZIER (Ed.), *The Central Nervous System and Behaviour*. New York: J. Macy.

LIFSCHITZ, W. (1958). Auditory evoked potentials in the central nervous system during acoustic habituation. Unpublished MS. quoted by HERNÁNDEZ-PEÓN (1960).

LINDSLEY, D. B. (1958). The reticular system and perceptual discrimination. In H. H. JASPER et al. (Ed.), *Reticular Formation of the Brain*. London: Churchill.

LINDSLEY, D. B. (1960). Attention, consciousness, sleep and wakefulness. In J. FIELD (Ed.), *Handbook of Physiology*. Washington: American Physiological Society.

LIVINGSTONE, R. B. (1960). Central control of receptors and sensory transmission systems. In J. FIELD (Ed.), *Handbook of Physiology*. Washington: American Physiological Society.

LONDON, I. D. (1954). Research on sensory interaction in the Soviet Union. *Psychol. Bull.*, **51**, 531–568.

LURIA, A. R. (1961). *The Role of Speech in the Regulation of Normal and Abnormal Behaviour*. Oxford: Pergamon Press.

LURIA, A. R. (1963). *The Mentally Retarded Child*. Oxford: Pergamon Press.

LYNN, R. (1963). Russian theory and research on schizophrenia. *Psychol. Bull.*, **60**, 486–498.

LYNN, R. and EYSENCK, H. J. (1963). Some effects of carisaprodol on pain reactivity. In H. J. EYSENCK (Ed.), *Experiments with Drugs*. Oxford: Pergamon Press.

MACLEAN, P. D. (1959). Interpolated remark in Grastyan's The hippocampus and higher nervous activity. In M. A. BRAZIER (Ed.), *The Central Nervous System and Behaviour*. New York: J. Macy.

MAGNES, J., MORUZZI, G. and POMPEIANO, O. (1961). Electroencephalogram-synchronizing structures in the lower brain stem. In G. E. W. WOLSTENHOLME and M. O'CONNOR (Eds.), *The Nature of Sleep*. London: Churchill.

MAGOUN, H. W. (1963). *The Waking Brain*. Illinois: C. C. Thomas.

MIHALEVSKAYA, L. I. (1958). Peculiarities of the relation between orientation and conditioned motor reactions in the determination of thresholds of visual sensitivity. In L. G. VORONIN et al. (Eds.), *The Orientation Reaction and Exploratory Behaviour*. Moscow: Acad. Pedag. Sciences.

MORISON, R. S. and DEMPSEY, E. W. (1942). A study of thalamo-cortical relations. *Amer. J. Physiol.*, **135**, 281–292.

MORRELL, F. (1961). Discussion of E. Grastyan's paper. In A. FESSARD et al. (Eds.), *Brain Mechanisms and Learning*. Oxford: Blackwell.

MORUZZI, G. (1960). Synchronizing influences of the brain stem and the inhibitory mechanisms underlying the production of sleep by sensory stimulation. In H. H. JASPER and G. D. SMIRNOV (Eds.), Moscow Colloquium on Electroencephalography of Higher Nervous Activity. *EEG Clin. Neurophysiol.*, Suppl. 13.

MORUZZI, G. and MAGOUN, H. W. (1949). Brain stem reticular formation and activation of the EEG. *EEG Clin. Neurophysiol.*, **1**, 455–473.

MOYER, K. E. (1963). Startle response: Habituation over trials and days, and sex and strain differences. *J. c.c.P.*, **56**, 863–865.

NARBUTOVICH, I. O. and PODKOPAEV, N. A. (1936). The conditioned reflex as an association. *Trudy Fiziol. Lab. Pavlova*, **6**, 5–25.

NEBYLITSIN, V. D. (1963). An electroencephalographic study of the parameters, strength of the nervous system and the equilibrium of the nervous processes in man, using a factor analysis. In B. M. TEPLOV (Ed.), *Typological Characteristics of Higher Nervous Activity in Man.* Vol. 3, Moscow: Acad. Pedag. Sciences, R.S.F.S.R.

NEBYLITSIN, V. D., ROZHDESTVENSKAYA, V. I. and TEPLOV, B. M. (1960). Concerning the interrelation between absolute sensitivity and the strength of the nervous system. *Quart. J. exp. Psychol.,* **12,** 17–25.

NIKITINA, G. M. (1954). Interrelations in the development of orientation reactions and conditioned motor reactions in ontogenesis. *Pavlov J. Higher Nerv. Act.,* **4,** 406–414.

NIKITINA, G. M. and NOVIKOVA, E. G. (1958). The effect of aminazin on the occurrence of the motor and vegetative components of conditioned defensive reactions in animals in ontogenesis. *Fourth Conference of Young Scientists of the Institute of Normal and Pathological Physiology.* Moscow.

NOTTERMAN, J. M. (1953). Experimental anxiety and a conditioned heart rate response in human beings. *Trans. N.Y. Acad. Sc.,* **16,** 24–33.

OBRAZTSOVA, L. F., POMAZANSKAYA, L. N., STEL'MAKH, V. A. and TROSHIKHIN, V. A. (1958). On the orientation reaction to neutral and signal stimuli in dogs and rabbits in ontogenesis. *The Orientation Reaction and Orienting-Investigating Activity.* Moscow. Acad. Pedag. Sciences. R.S.F.S.R.

OLDS, J. (1957). Self-stimulation experiments and differentiated reward systems. In H. H. JASPER *et al.* (Eds.), *Reticular Formation of the Brain.* London: Churchill.

OLDS, J. (1959). Interpolated remark in E. Grastyan's The hippocampus and higher nervous activity. In M. A. BRAZIER (Ed.), *The Central Nervous System and Behaviour.* New York: J. Macy.

OSWALD, I. (1962). *Sleeping and Waking.* Amsterdam: Elsevier.

PALESTRINI, M. and LIFSCHITZ, W. (1961). Functions of bulbo-pontine reticular formation and plastic phenomena in the central nervous system. In A. FESSARD *et al.* (Eds.), *Brain Mechanisms and Learning.* Oxford: Blackwell.

PAVLOV, I. P. (1927). *Conditioned Reflexes.* Oxford: Clarendon Press.

PETELINA, V. V. (1958). The vegetative component of the orientation reactions of the vestibule, visual and auditory analysors. *The Orientation Reaction and Orienting-Investigating Activity.* Moscow, Acad. Pedag. Sciences. R.S.F.S.R.

POLIAKOV, G. I. (1959). On the place of the reticular formation in the analyser systems. *Progress of Contemporary Biology,* **48,** 2.

POLIKANINA, R. I. and PROBOTOVA, L. E. (1958). On the question of identifying the orientation reaction in premature babies. *The Orientation Reaction and Orienting-Investigating Activity.* Moscow, Acad. Pedag. Sciences. R.S.F.S.R.

PROCTER, L. D., KNIGHTON, R. S. and CHURCHILL, J. A. (1957). Variations in consciousness produced by stimulating reticular formation of the monkey. *Neurology,* **7,** 193–203.

PROSSER, C. L. and HUNTER, W. S. (1936). The extinction of startle responses and spinal reflexes in the white rat. *Amer. J. Physiol.,* **117,** 609–618.

PURPURA, D. P. (1959). Contribution in discussion of E. Grastyan's The hippocampus and higher nervous activity. In M. A. BRAZIER (Ed.), *The Central Nervous System and Behaviour.* New York: J. Macy.

RAZRAN, G. (1961). The observable unconscious and the inferable conscious in current Soviet psychophysiology: interoceptive conditioning, semantic conditioning and the orienting reflex. *Psychol. Rev.,* **68,** 81–147.

ROGER, A., VORONIN, L. G. and SOKOLOV, E. N. (1958). An electroencephalographic investigation of the temporary connection during extinction of the orientation reaction in man. *Pavlov J. Higher Nerv. Act.*, **8**, 1–13.

ROGOV, A. A. (1955). A study of conditioned and unconditioned vascular reactions in man. *Works of the 8th All-Union Conference of Physiologists*. Moscow.

ROITBAK, A. I. (1960). Electrical phenomena in the cerebral cortex during the extinction of orientation and conditioned reflexes. In H. H. JASPER and G. D. SMIRNOV (Eds.), Moscow Colloquium on Electroencephalography of Higher Nervous Activity. *EEG Clin. Neurophysiol.*, Suppl. 13.

ROTHBALLER, A. B. (1955). Studies on the adrenalin sensitive component of the reticular activating system. McGill University Thesis.

ROZHDESTVENSKAYA, V. I. (1963). Determining the equilibrium of the fundamental nervous processes by the plethismographic method. In B. M. TEPLOV (Ed.), *Typological Characteristics of Higher Nervous Activity in Man*. Vol. 3, Moscow Acad. Pedag. Sciences. R.S.F.S.R.

ROZHDESTVENSKAYA, V. I., NEBYLITSIN, V. D., BORISOVA, M. N. and ERMOLAEVA-TOMINA, L. B. (1960). A comparative study of a number of indices of the strength of the nervous system in man. *Psychological Questions*, **5**, 41–56.

SHARPLESS, S. and JASPER, H. (1956). Habituation of the arousal reaction. *Brain*, **79**, 655–680.

SHLOLKIN-IARROS, E. G. (1958). Efferent paths from the visual cortex. *Pavlov J. Higher Nerv. Act.*, **8**, 114–128.

SOKOLOV, E. N. (1960). Neuronal models and the orienting reflex. In M. A. BRAZIER (Ed.), *The Central Nervous System and Behaviour*. New York: J. Macy.

SOKOLOV, E. N. (1963a). *Perception and the Conditioned Reflex*. Oxford: Pergamon Press.

SOKOLOV, E. N. (1963b). Higher nervous functions: the orienting reflex. *Ann. Rev. Physiology*, 1963.

SOLOVEICHIK, D. I. (1928). *Scientific Papers of the Pavlov Physiological Laboratories*, **2**, 2.

STAPLES, R. (1932). The response of infants to colours. *J. exp. Psychol.*, **15**, 479–496.

STRAUSS, H. (1929). Das Zusammenschrecken. *J. Psychol. Neurol.*, **39**, 111–231.

STRELTSOVA, N. L. (1955). The characteristics of some unconditioned reflexes in schizophrenics. In *Proceedings of the All Union Theoretical-Practical Conference dedicated to the Centenary of S. S. Korsakov and to Current Psychological Problems*. Moscow: Medgiz.

STRELTSOVA, N. L. (1958). The effect of certain physiological and pharmacological factors on the pupil component of the orientation reaction. *The Orientation Reaction and Orienting-Investigating Activity*. Moscow: Acad. Pedag. Sciences. R.S.R.S.R.

SYMONS, J. R. (1963). The effect of various heteromodal stimuli on visual sensitivity. *Quart. J. Exp. Psychol.*, **15**, 243–251.

TEPLOV, B. M. (1956). *Typological Characteristics of Higher Nervous Activity in Man*. Vol. 1. Moscow: Acad. Pedag. Sciences.

TEPLOV, B. M. (1959). *Typological Characteristics of Higher Nervous Activity in Man*. Vol. 2. Moscow: Acad. Pedag. Sciences.

TEPLOV, B. M. (1963). *Typological Characteristics of Higher Nervous Activity in Man*. Vol. 3. Moscow: Acad. Pedag. Sciences.

THOMPSON, R. F. and WELKER, W. I. (1963). Role of auditory cortex in reflex head orientation by cats to auditory stimuli. *J. comp. physiol. Psychol.*, **56**, 996–1002.

TINKLEPAUGH, O. L. (1928). An experimental study of representational factors in monkeys. *J. comp. Psychol.*, **8**, 197–236.

TISSOT, R. and MONNIER, M. (1961). Dualité du système thalamique de projection diffusé. *EEG Clin. Neurophysiol.*, **11**, 657–686.

UNGER, S. M. (1964). Habituation of the vasoconstrictive orienting reaction. *J. exp. Psychol.*, **67**, 11–18.

VALENTINE, C. W. (1914). The colour perception and colour preferences of an infant during its fourth and eighth months. *Brit. J. Psychol.*, **6**, 363–386.

VEDYAEV, F. P., and KARMANOVA, I. G. (1958). On the comparative physiology of the orientation reaction. *In the Orientation Reaction and Orienting-Investigating Activity*. Moscow: Acad. Pedag. Sciences. R.S.F.S.R.

VINOGRADOV, N. V. (1933). *Scientific Papers of the Pavlov Physiological Laboratories*, 5.

VINOGRADOVA, O. S. (1961). *The Orientation Reaction and its Neurophysiological Mechanisms*, Moscow: Acad. Pedag. Sciences. R.S.F.S.R.

VORONIN, L. G. (1962). Some results of comparative-physiological investigations of higher nervous activity. *Psychol. Bull.*, **59**, 161–195.

VORONIN, L. G. and SOKOLOV, E. N. (1960). Cortical mechanisms of the orienting reflex and its relation to the conditioned reflex. In H. H. JASPER and G. D. SMIRNOV (Eds.), Moscow Colloquium on Electroencephalography of Higher Nervous Activity. *EEG Clin. Neurophysiol.*, Suppl. 13.

VORONIN, L. G., SOKOLOV, E. N. and BAO-KHUA, U. (1959). Type features of the orientation reaction in man. *Voprosy Psikhologii*, **5**, 73–88.

YERKES, R. M. (1904). Inhibition and reinforcement of reaction in the frog Rana Clamitans. *J. comp. neurol. psychol.*, **14**, 124–137.

ZAGORYLKO, T. M. and SOLLERTINSKAYA, T. N. (1958). Towards a comparative analysis of the mechanisms of orientation reactions. *The Orientation Reaction and Orienting-Investigating Activity*. Moscow: Acad. Pedag. Sciences. R.S.F.S.R.

ZAPOROZHETS, A. V. (1961). The origin and development of conscious control of movements in man. In N. O'CONNOR (Ed.), *Recent Soviet Psychology*. Oxford: Pergamon Press.

AUTHOR INDEX

115

SUBJECT INDEX

117